Give Me Five!

ACTIVITY BOOK 6

macmillan education

Donna Shaw • Rob Sved

Unit S A new project

1 **Order the letters and write the words from the lesson.**

1 ____tunnel____ 2 ______________ 3 ______________

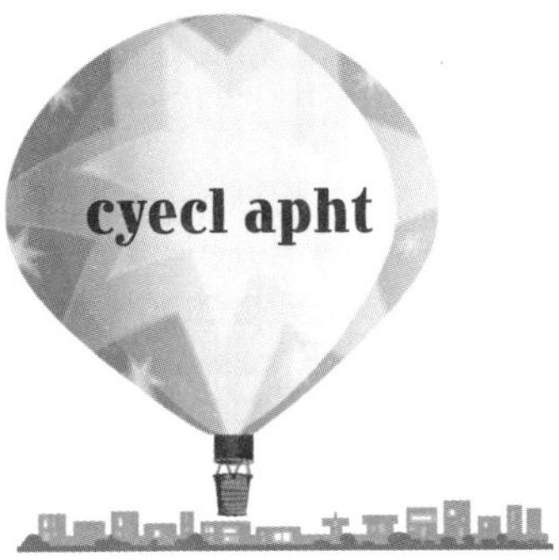

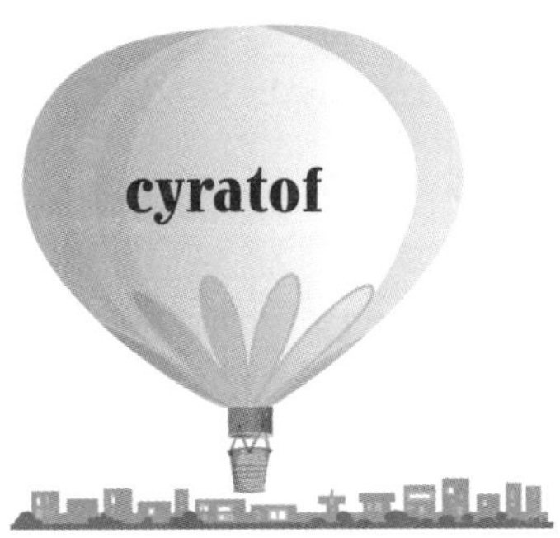

4 ______________ 5 ______________ 6 ______________

2 **Read and complete. Write one, two or three words.**

HOT-AIR BALLOON RIDES

Have you ever wanted to ride in a **1** ____hot-air balloon____? There are hot-air balloon rides all **2** ______________ in the park today. The hot-air balloon rises 150 metres so you'll have a fantastic view of **3** ______________. The tickets are £25 for adults and only £15 **4** ______________. However, all children must have **5** ______________ with them. The money will help protect local **6** ______________, so come along and have fun!

3 **Write about your town. Use *There is, There are, There isn't* or *There aren't*.** me

1 (cycle paths) There ______________________________ in my town.

2 (department store) ______________________________

3 (statues) ______________________________

4 (skate park) ______________________________

5 ______________________________

6 ______________________________

1 Read and circle the correct tense.

1 The children *wait* / *are waiting* to go up in the hot-air balloon now.

2 The ride *costs* / *is costing* £15 for children.

3 *Does Tom like* / *Is Tom liking* exciting activities?

4 The children *don't play* / *aren't playing* football at the moment.

5 Jess *doesn't carry* / *isn't carrying* a camera this morning.

6 *Do you prefer* / *are you preferring* hot-air balloons or planes?

7 Callum *wants* / *is wanting to* take a lot of photos.

2 Complete the sentences. Use the present simple or the present continuous.

1 Tom ____________________ (enjoy) doing exciting activities in his free time.

2 The children ________________________ (talk) about the hot-air balloon at the moment.

3 Jess ____________________ usually ____________________ (not go) to the park on Saturday morning.

4 ________________________ (rain) in the park now?

5 Emma ________________________ (not understand) Japanese.

6 ___________________ you ____________________ (want to) have a ride on a hot-air balloon this morning?

7 They ________________________ (make) videos of the children riding in a hot-air balloon now.

3 Write the questions. Use the present simple or the present continuous. Ask and answer.

1 What / you / usually do/ on Saturday morning? ______________________________

2 Why / it / important to protect the environment? ______________________________

3 What / you / wear / today? ______________________________

4 How often / you / take photos? ______________________________

5 What / you / think about / at the moment? ______________________________

6 you / prefer / indoor or outdoor activities? Why? ______________________________

4 What did you find out in Activity 3? Write about your partner.

My partner usually ______________________________

____

____

____

____

____

____

1 Find and circle the countries. Write.

1 Mexico

2 __________

3 __________

4 __________

5 __________

F	G	U	S	A	T	B	A
E	K	K	E	S	L	E	H
M	E	X	I	C	O	L	D
A	G	W	N	O	M	G	D
V	Y	B	C	T	A	I	I
O	P	U	H	L	U	U	L
R	T	E	I	A	S	M	J
Y	L	F	N	N	P	G	A
E	C	U	A	D	O	R	P
O	S	H	G	U	I	P	A
T	T	S	W	E	D	E	N

6 __________

7 __________

8 __________

9 __________

2 Which languages are spoken in these countries? Write sentences.

1 (China) Chinese is spoken in China.

2 (Japan) __________

3 (Scotland) __________

4 (Belgium) __________

5 (Egypt) __________

6 (Ecuador) __________

7 (Sweden) __________

3 Imagine your class wants to join the project. Complete the form for your class.

'Make a difference' project application form

Make a difference

1 Name of school:

2 Town: **3** Country:

4 Teacher's name:

5 Number of pupils in class: **6** Grade / course:

7 Why you want to join:

1 Read and answer the questions about the 'Make a difference' project.

1 Which part of England do the children live in?

They ______

2 Why are the birds in danger?

______

______

3 What did the children want to experience?

They ______

4 When did the children take the first photo?

They ______

5 What do the birds do in the nest boxes?

They ______

6 What do the children want to know?

They ______

2 Read and complete the questions.

~~isn't she~~ can he has he aren't I don't you does he can't he do they aren't you

1 She's from England, isn't she ?
2 You usually play basketball on Saturday, ______?
3 He hasn't got a pet, ______?
4 He can't speak German, ______?
5 You're eleven, ______?
6 I'm clever, ______?
7 He can ski, ______?
8 He doesn't like dancing, ______?
9 They don't live in the countryside, ______?

3 Complete the questions. Use question tags. Ask and answer.

1 You've got a skateboard, haven't you?
2 You don't like ______?
3 You can ______?
4 You aren't ______?
5 ______?
6 ______?
7 ______?

Unit 1 Travel trouble

1 Write the words and phrases in the puzzle.

1 _ _ _ _

2 _ _ _ _ _ _ _ _ _ _ _ _ _ _ _ _ _ _

3 r u n w a y

4 _ _ _ _ _ _ _ _ _

5 _ _ _ _ _ _ _ _

6 _ _ _ _ _ _ _ _ _ _ _ _ _ _

7 _ _ _ _ _ _ _ _

The mystery word is ______________________.

2 Read and complete the definitions.

1 ______arrivals______: This is the area of an airport which receives passengers after a flight has landed.

2 ____________________: This is the area of an airport which the passengers go through before a plane takes off.

3 ____________________: This is the place where you go to collect your boarding pass.

4 ____________________: This is a line of people who are waiting for something.

5 Hand luggage: ____________________

6 Trolley: ____________________

3 Read and remember the grammar in the lesson.

Which poster **would** you choose? I **would** choose the one about life at the airport.

4 Thinking skills Think of a poster you would like to make. Write the answers and the question.

1 What kind of poster would you make? ____________________

2 What materials would you use? ____________________

3 Who would you make the poster with? ____________________

4 What pictures would you include? ____________________

5 ____________________? I would put it on the classroom wall.

Which is the odd one out? Why? flight attendant / passenger / trolley / pilot

Past simple & past continuous with *while*

1 Read the sentences. Then underline the action which started first.

1 While we were walking around the airport, we saw a football player.
2 While they were entering the stadium, the match began.
3 Dad came home while we were having dinner.
4 I was playing football in the park when I saw the accident.
5 I heard a strange noise while I was cleaning the kitchen.
6 We were doing our homework when Greg called us.

2 Complete the sentences. Use the past simple or the past continuous.

1 My phone ___rang___ (ring) while I ___was pushing___ (push) the trolley.
2 The man ____________ (say) hello while we ____________ (wait) for our luggage.
3 While I ____________ (look for) my boarding pass, I ____________ (drop) my wallet.
4 My brother ____________ (sleep) when the plane ____________ (land).
5 It ____________ (rain) when we ____________ (arrive) at the airport.

3 Listen and circle A, B or C. CD1 8 Exams Practice

Visitors from Canada

1 Who did Carl meet at the airport?
A his brother **B** his cousins **C** his dad
2 Why did they arrive late at the airport?
A They got lost. **B** There was a lot of traffic. **C** They left home late.
3 How many of Carl's cousins are visiting?
A one **B** two **C** three
4 How many times has Carl been to Canada?
A never **B** once **C** twice
5 What's Carl going to do with them tomorrow?
A go hiking **B** play cricket **C** go skiing

4 Read and answer. Ask and answer. me

1 Do you have family or friends who live in a different city? Have they visited you before? ____________
2 Where did they come from? ____________
3 How did they get to your house? ____________

Which is the odd one out? Why? brother / uncle / aunt / father

After you read

1 Remember the article. Read and answer the questions.

1 What did Piccard promise in 1999? He ______________________

2 How long did it take to build the plane? It ______________________

3 What was Solar Impulse's first international journey? It ______________________

4 What was the weather like while it was landing? It ______________________

5 What did people do when the plane landed? They ______________________

6 Did the batteries have more or less energy when the plane landed? They ______________________

2 Listen and complete the notes. Write one, two or three words each time.

CD1 10

A PLANE THAT COULD **FLY FOREVER**

1 This article is about an explorer who is building planes that use energy ______________________.

2 Jess thinks it's a great story because Piccard is trying to fly ____________ without any ______________________.

3 For Jess, the best part is when the pilot is trying to ______________________ in Belgium.

4 Callum would like to find out more about what the plane ______________________.

5 Jess thinks it's interesting that the plane had ____________ energy when it landed than when it ____________.

6 Jess would recommend this to Tom because he likes articles about science ______________________.

3 Thinking skills What do you think of the article?

I think ______________________. I give it ____________ stars. ☆☆☆☆☆

4 Find out about Belgium with your family. ICT

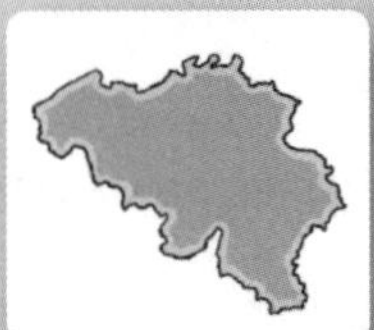

1 What are the three official languages in Belgium? ______________________

2 What countries have borders with Belgium? ______________________

3 Which dessert is Belgium famous for? ______________________

4 What did Adolphe Sax invent? ______________________

5 What are the three colours of the Belgian flag? ______________________

Which is the odd one out? Why? hot-air balloon / helicopter / rocket / speedboat

Verbs that are followed by the infinitive or the gerund

1 Read and circle the correct form.

1 Piccard decided *flying* / *to fly* a plane around the world.
2 Can you imagine *living* / *to live* in Australia?
3 John wants *reading* / *to read* that book.
4 Did you enjoy *helping* / *to help* at the café today?
5 I promised *doing* / *to do* my homework at the weekend.
6 Did Louie agree *looking* / *to look* after our dog?

2 Read and complete. Use the gerund or the infinitive form.

push ~~watch~~ buy play give

1 My mum enjoyed watching our school show.
2 I promised ________________ a computer game for my brother's birthday.
3 The flight attendant started ________________ food to the passengers.
4 John tried ________________ the trolley but he couldn't.
5 We stopped ________________ tennis at two o'clock.

3 Listen and write the words. Tick (✓) the correct box.

CD1 13

PRONUNCIATION

	/d/	/ɪd/	/t/
1 ________________	☐	☐	☐
2 ________________	☐	☐	☐
3 ________________	☐	☐	☐
4 ________________	☐	☐	☐
5 ________________	☐	☐	☐

4 Work with a partner. Write sentences about your friends. Use the time expressions and the verbs.

~~At lunchtime~~ Today This morning Yesterday

~~enjoy~~ decide try start suggest

1 At lunchtime, Leo enjoyed playing football.
2 ________________
3 ________________
4 ________________

For more grammar practice go to page 102.

Which is the odd one out? Why? promise / agree / decide / enjoy

1 **Read the sentences and complete the words.**

1 Twenty g ___ ___ sts were staying in the hotel.
2 We went upstairs in the l ___ ft.
3 The r ___ c ___ pt ___ ___ n ___ st at the hotel was very helpful.
4 This hotel has very good offers for b ___ ckp ___ ck ___ rs.
5 The g ___ ___ rd was helping the old lady on the pl ___ tf ___ rm.
6 'Let's ask for a map at the t ___ ___ r ___ st information c ___ ntr ___.'

2 **Read and complete. Write one word each time.** Exams Practice

A frozen hotel

ICEHOTEL is a hotel (1) ___in___ northern Sweden. The whole hotel is (2) ______________ of snow and ice and uses solar power for energy. It is built (3) ______________ November and December each year. Then, it opens for guests until the middle (4) ______________ April. In April, the hotel starts (5) ______________ melt and the water goes back into the river Torne. Inside the hotel, the walls, ceilings and furniture (6) ______________ all made of snow or ice. There are rooms for more (7) ______________ 100 guests. Usually, the guests sleep in the room for one night. They wear special clothes so they don't get cold and sleep in warm (8) ______________ bags, too. For the rest of their holiday, they stay in a warm hotel near the ICEHOTEL. During the day, the guests (9) ______________ walk around the hotel and see all of the rooms. Many of the rooms are designed (10) ______________ famous artists and the hotel is open all year, even in the summer!

3 **Read and learn.**

Word building

We often use a preposition after a verb. This may change the meaning of the verb.

The plane *takes off* at 3.30.

4 **Complete the sentences with a verb and a preposition.**

~~check~~ wash lie go try turn

off on ~~in~~ out up down

1 The first thing we need to do at the airport is to ___check in___.
2 It was my brother's turn to ______________.
3 Let's ______________ the television and play outside.
4 I'm going to ______________ these trousers in the changing room.
5 I don't feel well. I'm going to ______________ in bed.
6 Are you going to ______________ today or stay at home?

Which is the odd one out? Why? check-in desk / platform / ticket office / guard

After you read

1 Read and order the events.

He woke up and saw the icebergs.	☐	He fell asleep in the lifeboat.	☐
He climbed into the lifeboat.	☐	He watched the ship sinking.	☐
He and his aunt put on their lifejackets.	☐	He said goodbye to his uncle.	☐
He got on the ship at Southampton.	1	The ship hit an iceberg.	☐
He met the ship's captain.	☐		

2 Read the definitions and find the words in the text.

1 This verb means to get on a ship, a plane or a train (in the past tense). boarded
2 This is the highest floor of a ship that is outside. ______
3 This is a big room where people do exercise or play sport. ______
4 This is a small boat that people use to escape a sinking ship. ______
5 This is a group of musicians who play together. ______

3 Listen and circle A, B or C.

CD1 16 Exams Practice

The sinking of the Titanic

1 The Titanic didn't stop in this country.
A France B USA C Ireland

2 What happened 37 seconds after they saw the iceberg?
A The ship sank.
B They started to put people in the lifeboats.
C The ship hit the iceberg.

3 How many people died?
A More than 1500 B About 2200 C About 700

4 What has happened since the Titanic sank?
A All ships have space in their lifeboats for all the passengers.
B Dogs are not allowed on ships.
C Ships have space in their lifeboats for most of the passengers.

4 Cooperative learning Work with a partner. Imagine what it was like to be on the Titanic. Write three sentences.

______

______

______

Which is the odd one out? Why? calm / quiet / rough / silent

Develop your writing skills

1 Write sentences in the past tense. Use these verbs and nouns.

smell taste feel look ~~sound~~

~~music~~ cupcakes perfume people buildings

1 *The music sounded beautiful.*
2 ______
3 ______
4 ______
5 ______

Plan your writing

2 Cooperative learning Work with a partner. Plan your eyewitness account of a historical event. Make notes.

1 Name of historical event: ______
2 When did it happen? ______
3 Who was there? ______
4 What happened? ______
5 Who do you pretend to be for your eyewitness account? ______
6 What do you remember seeing? ______
7 What do you remember hearing or smelling? ______
8 How did you feel? ______
9 What's your reflection on the event? ______

3 Now write your eyewitness account in your notebook. Remember to use verbs of the senses to describe the event.

4 Learning to learn Read your eyewitness account to a new partner. Then check your work together. Put a tick (✓) or a cross (✗).

I've included the date. ☐
I've included an introduction. ☐
I've described the scene using the verbs of the senses. ☐
I've put the events in a clear order. ☐
I've used the past continuous tense correctly. ☐
I've finished the account with a reflection. ☐

Which is the odd one out? Why? touch / smell / taste / happy

1 Complete the conversation. Use expressions to show excitement. Act out.

What's the most interesting place you've visited? — I've been to Italy.

______________________! When did you go? — I went last summer.

Where did you stay? — We stayed on a campsite.

______________________! I love camping. — So, do I!

Prepare a conversation

2 Thinking skills Make notes about travel.

My travel

Where I've travelled to:
____
____
____

My most interesting places:
____
____
____

My future plans:
____
____
____

My opinions about travelling:
____
____
____

3 Write questions to ask a partner.

1 *What country would you like to visit?*
2 ______________________
3 ______________________
4 ______________________
5 ______________________

Have a conversation

4 Talk with your partner about travel.

Remember! Show excitement when your partner is speaking.

My progress

5 Reflect on the unit Read and complete the sentences.

In this unit I've learnt about ______________________

In this unit I've learnt to ______________________

I think that my work in Unit 1 is ______________________

The ways I can improve are ______________________

Which is the odd one out? Why? tent / sleeping bag / camping stove / hotel

Cooperative learning Work with a partner to do the quiz.

1 Write words that are related to these items.

1 airport: ______________ ______________ ______________

2 train station: ______________ ______________ ______________

3 ship: ______________ ______________ ______________

2 Read and complete the definitions.

1 The ____________________________ is the first place you go to when you enter a hotel.

2 The __________________ information ________________ is the place to go if you'd like a map of the town that you are in.

3 ______________________ travel between cities or countries carrying all their things on their backs.

3 Order and write the questions.

James: the new comic shop / Did you / while / see / walking home?/ you were

____

____

Tom: Yes, I did. I was there last Friday.

James: there? / buy / Did / anything / you

____

Tom: Yes, I bought two comics.

4 Infinitive or gerund? Look at the verbs and tick (✓) the correct option.

	+ to play	+ playing
decide	✓	☐
suggest	☐	☐
imagine	☐	☐

	+ to play	+ playing
enjoy	☐	☐
promise	☐	☐
agree	☐	☐

5 Read, remember and answer the questions.

1 What did the people in the orchestra do while the Titanic was sinking? ______________

2 When did the boy feel scared? ______________________________

6 Look and order the letters. What's the mystery word?

e g e c b r i

The mystery word is: ______________________

Definition: ____

Well done. Give me five!

Presenting balanced opinions and views

1 Listen to the conversations. Write the letters in the correct places. CD1 18

a It keeps you fit.
b Tickets might be expensive.
c It's not very good in bad weather.
d It is easier to travel up the hill.
e It is always on time.
f Fewer people will use the roads.
g It isn't always safe because of the cars.
h It's good for the environment.
i It is expensive to build.

Project 1: build a new cable car system.

Good things	Bad things
d	

Project 2: people use more bicycles.

Good things	Bad things

2 Cooperative learning Work in pairs. Read the instructions. Discuss and complete.

Write a sentence to explain your transport project for your town.
Then complete the chart with your balanced opinions.

Our transport project: ____________________

Good things	Bad things
____________	____________
____________	____________
____________	____________
____________	____________

Language bank

What do you think?

Why is it a good / bad thing?

But maybe …

I think that …

Really? Why?

I agree / disagree.

3 Explain your ideas to another group. Can they add more things to your chart?

4 Thinking skills Now decide if your project is a good idea or a bad idea.

Unit 2 Sports and hobbies

1 Read and write the sports.

1 ____________________
Place: indoors
Materials: gloves, masks, swords

2 ____________________
Place: running track and field
Materials: shorts, T-shirt and trainers

3 ____________________
Place: swimming pool
Materials: goal posts, a ball

4 ____________________
Place: gym
Materials: leotard, crash mats

5 ____________________
Place: outdoors
Materials: bow, arrows, target, gloves

6 ____________________
Place: gym
Materials: crash mats, belt

2 Read and complete the definitions.

1 ____________________: In this activity you jump up and down on a device made of metal and fabric.

2 ____________________: This object is oval shaped and it's got strings in the middle. You hold it in your hand when you play tennis.

3 ____________________: This object is made of strings which are tied together. You need to hit the ball over this when you play volleyball.

4 ____________________: This object is long and thin. It's usually made of cotton or nylon. You use it when you skip or go climbing.

5 crash mat: ____________________

6 hoop: ____________________

3 Read and remember the grammar in the lesson.

You **must** kick the ball. You **mustn't** touch the ball with your hands.

4 Read and answer about a sport you like. Can you guess your partner's sport?

1 Where do people do this sport? People ____________________

2 What materials do you need? ____________________

3 What must you do? ____________________

4 What mustn't you do? ____________________

Which is the odd one out? Why? tennis / rugby / archery / cricket

1 Read and complete the questions. Use the correct form of the verbs. Ask and answer.

Present perfect & past simple questions

play do go do ~~go~~ do

1 Have you ever ___been___ horse riding?
2 Have you ever ________ volleyball?
3 Have you ever ________ judo?
4 ________________ trampolining?
5 ________________ mountain biking?
6 ________________ archery?

2 Read the sentences and write questions. Use the past simple.

1 I've been sailing. Where ________________?
2 I've been jogging. When ________________?
3 I've tried fencing. Did ________________?
4 I've played rugby. Was ________________?

3 Listen and write the letter.

CD1 22

Exams Practice

When did Sally do these activities?

		A last year
1 sailing	☐	**B** last summer
2 horse riding	☐	**C** two months ago
3 volleyball	☐	**D** yesterday
4 rock climbing	☐	**E** the day before yesterday
5 archery	☐	**F** last weekend
		G a couple of years ago

4 Read and answer. Ask and answer.

1 What's the most exciting sport you've done? ________________
2 When did you do it? ________________
3 What was it like? ________________

Which is the odd one out? Why? cycling / ice hockey / jogging / horse riding

After you read

1 Remember the information. Read and answer the questions.

1 When did kung fu begin? It ____________________

2 What did the Shaolin monks want to defend? They ____________________

3 Where have the Shaolin monks appeared? They ____________________

4 Which kung fu style helps you to balance? The ____________________

5 How many hours do the trainee monks sleep? They ____________________

6 Why do you think the monks are good at football? Because ____________________

2 Listen and complete the notes. Write one, two or three words each time.

CD1 24

Kung Fu

1 Callum thinks that the information is ____________________.

2 Jess saw the Shaolin monks____________________.

3 Callum says that there are ____________________ of kung fu.

4 Jess learns that a crane is a bird that has ____________________.

5 Callum thinks that the ____________________ style of kung fu is the coolest.

6 Callum wouldn't become a trainee Shaolin monk because he doesn't like ____________________.

3 Thinking skills What do you think of the information?

I think ____________________. I give it __________ stars. ☆☆☆☆☆

4 Find out about China with your family.

ICT

1 How many stars are on the Chinese flag? ____________________

2 What's the longest river in China? ____________________

3 How long's the Great Wall of China? ____________________

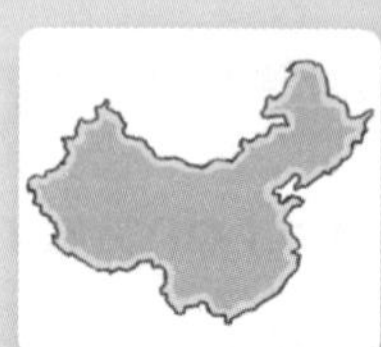

4 Where do giant pandas live? ____________________

5 What's China's largest city? ____________________

Which is the odd one out? Why? leopard / elephant / dragon / crane

Present perfect

1 Write the sentences in the present perfect. Use *for* or *since*.

1 play chess (six years) I've played chess for six years.

2 know my friend (I was three) I ______

3 do gymnastics (last year) He ______

4 have short hair (two days) She ______

2 Read and write the questions.

1 How long have you ______? I've lived in this town since I was born.

2 ______? She's studied French for ten months.

3 ______? They've played in the team since September.

4 ______? He's liked football since he was five.

5 ______? He's done kung fu for four years.

3 Underline the stressed words in the sentences. Listen and check.

CD1 27

PRONUNCIATION

1 I've played the violin for two years.

2 How long have they studied English?

3 She's been ill since Saturday.

4 He's worn glasses for six months.

5 I've had a dog since last year.

6 How long has she known her friend?

4 Read and answer the questions. Ask and answer.

1 How long have you studied at this school?

I've ______

2 How long have you known your best friend?

______

3 How long have you lived in your house?

______

4 How long have you watched your favourite TV programme?

______

5 How long have you done your favourite sport?

______

For more grammar practice go to page 103.

Which is the odd one out? Why? one month / September / five years / one hour

1 Cooperative learning **Choose four hobbies from the lesson which you think are interesting. Compare with a partner.**

I think doing needlework is more interesting than collecting cards.

I totally disagree.

2 **Read the text and the sentences. Write *A* (right), *B* (wrong) or *C* (doesn't say).** Exams Practice

Stamp collecting

Do you know that more than 200 million people around the world enjoy stamp collecting? The first stamp appeared in Britain in 1840 and it was called the Penny Black. It had a picture of the queen of England on the front, but it didn't have a sticky back. People had to use their own glue to stick it to the envelope. Nowadays, more than 200 countries around the world produce their own stamps and some of them are miniature works of art. There have been lots of unusual stamps too. The Pacific island of Tonga once issued banana-shaped stamps and Australia issued stamps that looked like precious stones. However, the prize for the most unusual stamp goes to Bhutan. This country once produced stamps that looked like a record and you could actually play them on a record player!

1. The first stamp appeared more than 200 years ago. B
2. The Penny Black was a black stamp. ☐
3. Some stamps have beautiful drawings on them. ☐
4. Stamps are always rectangular. ☐
5. The Australian stamps were very expensive. ☐
6. You could listen to stamps from Bhutan. ☐

3 **Read and learn.**

Word building

A suffix is a group of letters that is added to the end of a word.

You can add *-er* or *-or* to some verbs to make the names of the people who do the actions.

to collect – a collect*or*
to teach – a teach*er*

4 **Add *-er* or *-or* to change these verbs into nouns.**

1 to play: ___a player___
2 to design: ______
3 to instruct: ______
4 to report: ______
5 to act: ______
6 to direct: ______
7 to clean: ______
8 to sail: ______
9 to decorate: ______

Which is the odd one out? Why? footballs / stamps / stickers / posters

After you read

1 Which questions does the text answer? Tick (✓) or cross (✗).

1 When was Gisela born? ✓
2 When did she begin to kitesurf? ☐
3 Why did Gisela move to Tarifa? ☐
4 What was her favourite school subject? ☐
5 What's the most difficult kitesurf trick? ☐
6 When was she world champion the first time? ☐
7 What's Gisela like? ☐
8 How many times has she been world champion? ☐

2 Look at Activity 1. Write a paragraph using answers for the questions that you have ticked (✓).

Gisela was born ____________________

____

____

____

____

3 Listen and complete the leaflet about safety on the water. CD1 30

Safety on the water

Remember these simple rules so that you and other people have a safe and fun time on the water.

Always

Wear a **1** ____________, a lifejacket and a quick release harness.

Check your **2** ____________ and repair any damage.

Carry a **3** ____________ so you can cut your kite strings.

Check the **4** ____________ before you ride.

Never

Ride too **5** ____________ from the shore.

Practise **6** ____________ next to the beach.

Kitesurf in a **7** ____________ area.

4 Find out two more facts about Gisela Pulido. Write sentences. ICT

1 ____________________

2 ____________________

Which is the odd one out? Why? kayaking / water-skiing / skiing / windsurfing

Develop your writing skills

1 Complete the sentences. Use an adjective.

enormous fascinating brilliant astonishing

1 The report about Gisela Pulido was ________________. I learnt lots of interesting facts.

2 Gisela's kite is ________________. It collects lots of wind.

3 I think Ross Lynch is a ________________ actor.

4 It's ________________ to learn that all Ross Lynch's family have names that begin with the letter R.

Plan your writing

2 Cooperative learning Work with a partner. Plan your magazine article about a famous person. Make notes.

1 Title: ________________

2 Famous person: ________________

3 What's he / she famous for? ________________

4 When was he / she born? ________________

5 What did he / she do first? ________________

6 What has he / she done since then? ________________

7 Interesting facts: ________________

8 Opinion: ________________

3 Now write your magazine article in your notebook. Remember to use extreme adjectives.

4 Learning to learn Read your magazine article to a new partner. Then check your work together. Put a tick (✓) or a cross (✗).

- I've included a title. ☐
- I've introduced my famous person. ☐
- I've included biographical information. ☐
- There are some interesting facts. ☐
- I've given an opinion. ☐
- I've used one or more extreme adjectives. ☐

Which is the odd one out? Why? huge / enormous / tiny / massive

1 **Read the situation. What do you need to say? Write.**

1 A friend is whispering. You can't hear her. *Can you* ______________________

2 Your English friend is speaking too fast. ______________________

3 You didn't hear what the teacher said. ______________________

Prepare a conversation

2 **Thinking skills** **Make notes about your favourite sports.**

Favourite sports

Sports I enjoy doing:
____
____
____

Sports I enjoy watching:
____
____
____

My favourite team / sports person:
____
____
____

Sports I'd like to try:
____
____
____

3 **Write questions to ask a partner.**

1 *Are you sporty?* ______________________

2 ______________________

3 ______________________

4 ______________________

5 ______________________

Have a conversation

4 **Talk with your partner about your favourite sports.**

Remember! Tell people when it's difficult to understand them.

My progress

5 **Reflect on the unit** **Read and complete the sentences.**

In this unit I've learnt about ______________________

In this unit I've learnt to ______________________

I think that my work in Unit 2 is ______________________

The ways I can improve are ______________________

Which is the odd one out? Why? racket / net / bat / stick

Cooperative learning Work with a partner to do the quiz.

1 Write the equipment you need for these sports.

1 archery: ______________________________

2 fencing: ______________________________

3 badminton: ______________________________

2 Write about what you have or haven't done. Use the present perfect.

1 (karate) I ______________________________

2 (football) ______________________________

3 (horse riding) ______________________________

3 Look and write the words in the chart.

a week   last week   ~~five minutes~~   a long time   five o'clock   16th August   half an hour   I was ten

for	since
five minutes	

4 Write the questions and answers. Use *for* or *since*.

1 (study English) How long have you ______________________________

I've ______________________________

2 (live in your town) ______________________________

____

3 (know your English teacher) ______________________________

____

5 Read, remember and answer the questions.

1 How long have the Shaolin monks done kung fu? ______________________________

2 How long has Ross Lynch appeared on TV? ______________________________

6 Look and order the letters. What's the mystery word?

s i a s t o n i n g h

The mystery word is: ______________________________

Definition: ______________________________

Well done. Give me five!

Achieving your goals

1 Listen to the conversations. Tick (✓) the correct answer.

CD1 32

① A What sport does Tony do?

- ☐ volleyball
- ☐ football
- ☐ basketball

B Why does he want to give up the sport?

- ☐ He thinks he isn't very good.
- ☐ He thinks it's too difficult.
- ☐ He isn't the best.

C What advice does the teacher give?

- ☐ Practise more.
- ☐ Be patient.
- ☐ Believe in yourself.

② A What hobby does Dina do?

- ☐ singing
- ☐ drawing
- ☐ drama

B Why does she want to give up?

- ☐ Her friend is better.
- ☐ She makes a lot of mistakes.
- ☐ She isn't artistic.

C What advice does her mum give?

- ☐ Learn from your friends.
- ☐ Learn from your mistakes.
- ☐ Keep trying.

2 Thinking skills Read what people say when an activity is difficult. Are they being positive (P) or negative (N)?

① I can't do it better. [N]

② I'm going to work harder. ☐

③ I can learn from my mistakes. ☐

④ I can try a different strategy. ☐

⑤ I'm not good enough. ☐

⑥ This needs a bit more time, but that's OK. ☐

3 Read, think and answer. Be positive!

1 What are you good at? I'm good at ____________________

2 What can you do to be even better? I can ____________________

3 What activity is difficult for you? ____________________ is difficult for me.

4 What can you do to be better? I can ____________________

4 Now share the information with a partner.

I'm good at drawing, but I can do better in sport.

Tennis is difficult for me, but I'm good at football.

Unit 3 Healthy habits

1 Find and circle the words. Complete the chart.

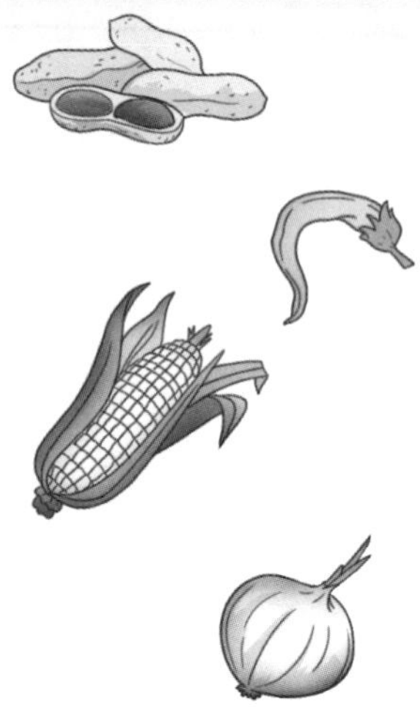

P	V	P	A	M	G	B	E	G	Q	O	Y	S	H	X
R	L	E	H	V	K	L	A	J	H	P	N	M	T	V
A	Z	A	Q	P	O	R	S	I	U	Z	D	I	N	E
W	D	N	D	Q	L	C	R	E	R	B	J	P	O	Y
N	R	U	L	I	T	Q	A	T	U	R	K	E	Y	N
S	G	T	C	L	N	Q	T	D	N	D	E	J	D	E
W	C	S	T	R	G	F	S	B	O	D	J	G	Z	V
W	D	J	O	T	C	O	S	F	S	D	F	G	C	T
H	P	C	P	T	Y	Z	Q	H	S	R	A	C	R	C
C	H	I	L	L	I	P	E	P	P	E	R	X	C	W

Countable noun	Uncountable noun
peanuts	

2 Read and complete the definitions.

1 ____________________: This is a hard brown spice. It's made into powder and added to savoury and sweet food.

2 ____________________: This is meat from a bird. The bird is bigger than a chicken. People eat this at Christmas.

3 ____________________: This is a fruit and is small and green. Its juice is used in cooking.

4 ____________________: These are seeds of plants that are cooked and eaten. They are often white, brown or black.

5 Onion: ____

6 Beef: ____

3 Read and remember the grammar in the lesson.

Are there **any** oranges in the fridge? Yes, there are. / No, there aren't.
Is there **any** lemonade in the fridge? Yes, there is. / No, there isn't.

4 Look at Activity 3. Think about the food in your fridge. Ask and answer.

Which is the odd one out? Why? carrot / flour / biscuit / pear

too & enough with countable and uncountable nouns

1 **Look at the recipe and the ingredients. Read the sentences. Write *right* or *wrong*.**

Meatballs

- 800g beef
- 2 cloves of garlic
- 2 onions
- 8 tomatoes
- 50g flour

1 There is too much garlic. wrong

2 There isn't enough flour. ______

3 There aren't enough onions. ______

4 There are too many tomatoes. ______

2 **Look at Activity 1 and write true sentences.**

1 (garlic) There isn't enough garlic.

2 (beef) ______

3 (onions) ______

4 (tomatoes) ______

3 **Listen and complete the notes.** CD1 36 Exams Practice

Cookery lessons

Club: The Cookery Club

Day: (1) ______

Place: (2) ______

Time: (3) ______

Number of pupils: (4) ______

Style of cookery: (5) ______ and Chinese

4 **Read and answer. Ask and answer.**

1 Do you like cooking? How often do you cook? ______

2 What can you cook? ______

3 What clubs are there at your school? ______

5 **Think about your school. Tick (✓) the sentence that is true for you.**

There are too many clubs in our school. ☐ There aren't enough clubs in our school. ☐

Which is the odd one out? Why? knife / jar / bottle / bag

3 Lesson 3 **Culture around the world: Mexico**

After you read

1 Remember the story. Read and answer the questions.

1 What did the farmers do to the beans before they mixed them with water? They ____________________

2 Who did the farmers believe the drink was given by? They ____________________

3 Where was Hernán Cortés from? He ____________________

4 What did Cortés suggest adding to the drink? He ____________________

5 When did people begin to make bars of chocolate? People ____________________

6 Where do cocoa trees need to grow? They ____________________

2 Listen and complete the notes. Write one, two or three words each time.

CD1 38

The food of the gods

1 The story is about where chocolate ____________________ ____________________.

2 Callum thought that the Mayans made the ____________________ into chocolate bars.

3 Tom's learnt that chocolate bars were invented much ____________________ than drinking chocolate.

4 Tom thinks it's interesting that Cortés thought the drink was ____________________.

5 Callum didn't know that half of the world's cocoa beans grow in ____________________.

6 Tom thinks it is strange that Callum ____________________ chocolate.

3 Thinking skills What do you think of the story?

I think ____________________.

I give it ____________ stars. ☆☆☆☆☆

4 Find out about Mexico with your family. ICT

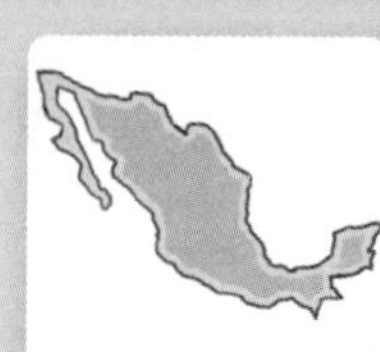

1 What's the capital city of Mexico? ____________________

2 What year were the Olympic Games in Mexico? ____________________

3 What's the population of Mexico? ____________________

4 What are Frida Kahlo and Diego Rivera famous for? ____________________

5 What was the Aztec word for chocolate? ____________________

Which is the odd one out? Why? bitter / salty / sweet / bright

Modal verbs

1 Complete the sentences. Use *need to, needn't* or *mustn't*.

1 You ______________ look carefully before you cross the road.
2 You ______________ go to the supermarket to buy food. You can use the Internet.
3 People ______________ drive faster than the speed limit.
4 The project is due in the morning so we ______________ finish it today.
5 'I told you that you ______________ hit your brother!'

2 Match the sentence halves.

1 You needn't bring a football with you	☐	a before the shops close.
2 You shouldn't eat too many sweets	☐	b because we've got lots of them.
3 We should leave the house now	☐	c because it's warm outside.
4 You need to wash your hands	☐	d after you cut chicken.
5 We needn't wear our coats	☐	e because they are bad for your teeth.

3 Underline the silent letters in each word. Listen and check. Which word has got two silent letters?

CD1 41

PRONUNCIATION

1 wouldn't	3 island	5 whistle	7 guest	9 mustn't
2 listen	4 white	6 plumber	8 knife	10 answer

4 Work with a partner. Think and write sentences about a park for children. Use *can, needn't, need to, mustn't, should* or *shouldn't*.

1 (use the recycling bins) ______________________________
2 (ride your bike on the path) ______________________________
3 (climb the trees) ______________________________
4 (be careful near the lake) ______________________________
5 (keep your dog on a lead) ______________________________
6 (play football in the field) ______________________________

For more grammar practice go to page 104.

Which is the odd one out? Why? whistle / chocolate / mustn't / listen

1 Find and circle the words. Complete the actions.

K	E	M	Y	D	B	F	K
Z	B	X	T	R	O	O	R
U	R	E	S	T	X	O	O
D	S	P	E	N	D	D	F
W	R	F	E	A	T	I	O
B	Q	I	Q	T	Z	T	G
X	Z	H	N	Z	B	G	J
O	Z	V	Y	K	N	R	M

1 ______________ water
2 ______________ for walks
3 eat junk ______________
4 ______________ exercise
5 ______________ time on the computer
6 ______________ fruit and vegetables
7 drink ______________ drinks
8 ______________

2 Read the sentences about Sam. Choose the correct word (A, B or C). Exams Practice

Sam's lifestyle

1 Sam's got quite a healthy lifestyle. He ______________ exercise every day.
A does **B** makes **C** goes

2 He plays football ______________ the weekend, too.
A by **B** at **C** in

3 How ______________ does Sam eat fruit and vegetables?
A much **B** many **C** often

4 He loves vegetables and eats them with every ______________.
A plate **B** food **C** meal

5 Sam goes to bed late so he doesn't have ______________ rest.
A too **B** enough **C** many

6 His mum thinks he ______________ go to bed earlier.
A would **B** needs **C** should

3 Read and learn.

Word building

Words that have opposite meanings are called **antonyms**.

4 Write the antonyms for these words.

disgusting ~~bitter~~ still smooth difficult ugly

1 sweet: *bitter*
2 beautiful: ______________
3 delicious: ______________
4 rough: ______________
5 easy: ______________
6 fizzy: ______________

5 Write the antonyms for these words. What do they have in common?

1 popular: ______________
2 healthy: ______________
3 kind: ______________
4 tidy: ______________

Which is the odd one out? Why? fantastic / incredible / amazing / nice

After you read

1 Read and write *L* (Luke), *O* (Olivia) or *N* (neither).

1 Fast food is great when you are in a hurry. ☐
2 There's no variety in fast food. It's always the same. ☐
3 If we eat fast food all the time, we'll lose traditional recipes. ☐
4 Fast food is much healthier these days. ☐
5 We're not sure what we are eating when we eat fast food. ☐
6 Fast food is always cheaper than home-made food. ☐

2 Read the definitions and find the words in the text.

1 These are items of food you use when you make something to eat. ingredients
2 We add this to make food or drink sweet. ______
3 This is an explanation of how to cook something to eat. ______
4 This adjective means that you have a lot of things to do. ______
5 This is another word for 'choices'. ______
6 This word is the antonym of 'more expensive'. ______

3 Listen to the questionnaire and tick (✓) Leah's answers.

CD2 2

1 How often do you eat fast food?
never ☐ once a month ☐ once every 2–3 weeks ☐ once every 1–2 weeks ☐
once or twice a week ☐ Other: ______

2 What fast food do you eat?
pizza ☐ burgers ☐ fish and chips ☐ sandwiches ☐ Other: ______

3 What do you like about fast food?
it's cheap ☐ it's fast ☐ it tastes good ☐

4 Where do you eat fast food?
at the fast food restaurant ☐ at home ☐ in the park ☐ at the beach ☐ in the street ☐

5 Do you think fast food is bad for you?
always ☐ usually ☐ sometimes ☐ occasionally ☐ never ☐

4 Cooperative learning Work with a partner. Look at Activity 3. Ask and answer.

Which is the odd one out? Why? carrot / orange / pumpkin / lime

Develop your writing skills

1 Complete the sentences. Use the connective words and phrases.

However ~~Firstly~~ Furthermore On the other hand on the one hand

1 There are many benefits to running. ___Firstly___, running can be good for your heart …
2 So, ________, computer games can help improve many skills. ________, playing them won't give you any physical exercise.
3 Travelling by car can be quick and comfortable. ________, it can also be bad for the environment.
4 There are many arguments for wearing a school uniform. Firstly, children won't worry about the clothes they are wearing. ________, a school uniform always looks tidier.

Plan your writing

2 Cooperative learning Work with a partner. Plan your argument text. Make notes.

1 What's the topic? ________
2 What are the arguments for this? ________
____
3 What are the arguments against this? ________
____
4 Key phrases to introduce the arguments: ________
5 Connectives to contrast the arguments: ________
6 Your opinion: ________

3 Now write your argument text in your notebook. Remember to use connective words or phrases.

4 Learning to learn Read your text to a new partner. Then check your work together. Put a tick (✓) or a cross (✗).

I've included an introduction. ☐
I've included arguments for both sides. ☐
I've given a summary. ☐
I've used connective words and phrases. ☐
I've written the points of the argument clearly. ☐
I've included my own opinion. ☐

Which is the odd one out? Why? furthermore / everyone / also / however

1 Order the conversation. Act out.

What do you do to keep healthy? Do you do exercise? [1]

That's the same as me! Do you usually eat healthily? [ ]

I do, too. How often do you do dance? [ ]

I do it three times a week. [ ]

We eat a lot of fruit and vegetables. I don't have many snacks between lunch and dinner. [ ]

Yes, I do. I love dancing. [ ]

Prepare a conversation

2 Thinking skills Make notes about your health.

My health

Keeping fit:

____

____

____

Rest and relaxation:

____

____

____

Eating healthily:

____

____

____

Going to the doctor's:

____

____

____

3 Write questions to ask a partner.

1 *Do you get enough rest?*

2 ______________________

3 ______________________

4 ______________________

5 ______________________

Have a conversation

4 Talk with your partner about your health.

Remember!
Use phrases to agree with your partner.

My progress

5 Reflect on the unit Read and complete the sentences.

In this unit I've learnt about ______________________

In this unit I've learnt to ______________________

I think that my work in Unit 3 is ______________________

The ways I can improve are ______________________

Which is the odd one out? Why? tour guide / doctor / nurse / dentist

Cooperative learning Work with a partner to do the quiz.

1 Write the words from the unit.

1 nacnnimo: ____________ 4 wrapns: ____________
2 eilm: ____________ 5 doovaca: ____________
3 kteruy: ____________ 6 ihllic rpeepp: ____________

2 Write the verbs.

1 ____________ exercise 4 ____________ for walks
2 ____________ fruit and vegetables 5 ____________ fizzy drinks
3 ____________ water 6 ____________ junk food

3 Read and complete the sentences.

isn't enough aren't enough is too much ~~are too many~~

1 There ___*are too many*___ tomatoes in the box.
2 There ____________ oranges in the box.
3 There ____________ milk in the bottle.
4 There ____________ water in the bowl.

4 Read and complete.

needn't need to mustn't ~~must~~ shouldn't should

1 Obligation to do something: ___*must*___ ____________
2 Obligation **not** to do something: ____________
3 Advice to do something: ____________
4 Advice **not** to do something: ____________
5 No obligation: ____________

5 Read, remember and answer the questions.

1 What are the two sides of an argument? For and ____________
2 What did Luke say was sometimes used to thicken sauces and milkshakes? ____________

6 Look and order the letters. What's the mystery word?

h o o c c t e l a

The mystery word is: ____________

Definition: ____________

Well done. Give me five!

GIVE ME FIVE!

Recording information and setting routines

1 **Listen to the conversation. Complete the exercise calendars.** CD2 4

	Morning		Afternoon	
	Maddie	Tom	Maddie	Tom
Monday				
Tuesday				
Wednesday				
Thursday				
Friday				
Saturday				
Sunday				

2 **Complete these sentences. Then listen again and check.** CD2 4

You could ~~else~~ What exercise Tell me Why don't you

Do you do anything _else_ ?

<u>Asking for information</u>

________________ about your routine.

________________ do you do?

<u>Making suggestions</u>

________________ go swimming.

________________ try another sport?

3 **Work in pairs. Complete an exercise calendar for your partner. Then compare your calendars with another pair. Who is going to do the most exercise?**

________________'s exercise calendar

	Morning	Afternoon
Monday		
Tuesday		
Wednesday		
Thursday		
Friday		
Saturday		
Sunday		

An energy proposal

1 **Listen and complete the notes.** CD2 5

turns electricity produce heat river turbines

Renewable energy – where does it come from?

1 **Solar energy**

Solar panels are used to ______________ water.

Solar cells are used to change solar energy into ______________.

2 **Wind energy**

Wind ______________ are used to ______________ electricity.

3 **Hydroelectric energy**

This comes from water in a ______________. The water ______________ a turbine and this produces electricity.

2 **Cooperative learning** **Work in groups and make notes on each renewable energy.**

Solar energy	Wind energy	Hydroelectric energy
Advantages:	Advantages:	Advantages:
Disadvantages:	Disadvantages:	Disadvantages:
Impact on the environment:	Impact on the environment:	Impact on the environment:

1 **Work in groups. Plan your group's digital presentation.**

A proposal for renewable energy

Which renewable energy are you proposing and why?

____

____

____

____

____

What could you build? ______________________________

Where could you put it? ______________________________

Is it good for the environment? Why? ______________________

We could use the energy to ______________________________

Reflect on your project

2 **Read and answer.**

1 Write three things you learnt about renewable energy.

____

____

____

2 Why were you a good group member? Write two things.

____

____

3 What could your group do better for the next project?

____

4 What mark would you give your group's work? ______ /10

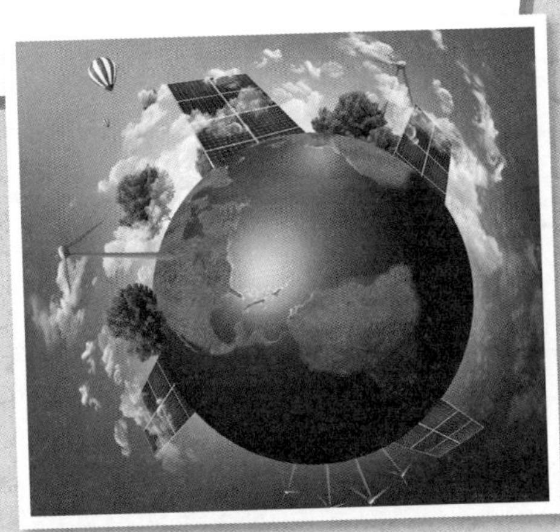

Unit 4 Creative kids

1 Find, circle and write the creative activities.

Do

1 origami

2 ______________

Create

3 an ______________

A	T	C	D	D	U	I	Z	X	L
O	J	E	W	E	L	L	E	R	Y
G	O	R	I	G	A	M	I	D	S
L	P	A	Q	C	G	W	W	O	A
S	I	M	A	D	T	F	A	K	L
A	N	I	M	A	T	I	O	N	P
E	U	C	A	F	P	L	A	Y	E
T	Y	S	I	O	B	M	B	D	W

Make

4 ______________

5 a ______________

Perform

6 a ______________

2 Read and complete the definitions.

1 ______________: When you do this activity you do a dance that is typical of your country or your region.

2 ______________: This is a small object that looks like a person or an animal. You can use your hands or some strings to move it.

3 ______________: This is the place where actors stand when they perform a play.

4 ______________: These are special clothes that dancers or actors wear on stage or in a film.

5 beads: ______________

6 clay: ______________

3 Read and remember the grammar in the lesson.

I **have done** ceramics. I **have never composed** a song. I **haven't composed** a song.

4 Write about the creative activities you have and haven't done. (me)

1 ______________

2 ______________

3 ______________

4 ______________

5 ______________

6 ______________

Which is the odd one out? Why? a film / origami / ceramics / traditional dancing

Past passive

1 Complete the sentences. Use the past passive.

paint ~~make~~ sing write create film

1 Originally, shadow puppets ___were made___ in China.
2 *Matilda* ______________ by Roald Dahl.
3 Mickey and Minnie ______________ by Walt Disney.
4 *The Hobbit* ______________ in New Zealand.
5 *Guernica* ______________ by Picasso.
6 *Earth Song* ______________ by Michael Jackson.

2 Change the sentences from the active form to the past passive.

1 William Shakespeare wrote *Hamlet*.
Hamlet was ______________
2 James Cameron made *Titanic* and *Avatar*.
____
3 Matt Groening created *The Simpsons*.
____
4 Mozart composed *The Marriage of Figaro*.
____

3 Listen and complete the notes.

CD2 9 Exams Practice

The Hobbit

The book was written by (1) ______________. It was published in (2) ______________.
The first film was released in (3) ______________. It was filmed in (4) ______________.
In the first weekend, it was watched by almost (5) ______________ million people in North America.

4 Choose four verbs and write true sentences. Use the past passive form.

write paint ~~sing~~ create make perform

1 ______________ was ___sung___ by ______________.
2 ______________
3 ______________
4 ______________

Which is the odd one out? Why? actor / audience / singer / musician

After you read

1 Remember the information. Read and answer the questions.

1 What does the word *manga* mean? It ____________________

2 When was manga created? It ____________________

3 Where do you begin reading a manga comic? You ____________________

4 When do manga characters go red? They ____________________

5 Who was *Spirited Away* made by? It ____________________

6 Which prize did it win? It ____________________

2 Listen and complete the notes. Write one, two or three words each time.

CD2 11

Manga magic

1 Jess thinks that the information is ____________________.

2 Callum doesn't like the characters' ____________________.

3 Jess enjoys ____________________.

4 Callum doesn't like reading comics from ____________________.

5 Jess ____________________ reading the story frames from right to left.

6 Callum has watched the *Dragon Ball* series for ____________________.

3 Thinking skills What do you think of the information?

I think ____________________. I give it __________ stars. ☆☆☆☆☆

4 Find out about Japan with your family. ICT

1 Which three countries are the nearest to Japan? ____________________
____

2 How many volcanoes are there in Japan? ____________________

3 Name three Japanese martial arts: ____________________

4 Name three things that are produced in Japan: ____________________

5 What do people use when they do ikebana? ____________________

Which is the odd one out? Why? novel / comic / film / poem

Past passive questions

1 Order and write the questions.

1 *James Bond* / was / filmed? / Where

Where was James Bond filmed?

2 by? / *Your Name* / was / Who / written

___

3 the concerts / performed? / were / Where

___

4 the play / When / written? / was

___

5 this picture / Who / drawn / was / by?

___

2 Read the answers. Write the questions.

1 Where ___?

Dragon Ball was created in Japan.

2 ___?

The films were made in Scotland.

3 ___?

Romeo and Juliet was written by Shakespeare.

4 ___?

The songs were recorded two years ago.

5 ___?

Imagine was sung by John Lennon.

3 Read the sentences. Underline the silent 'w' sounds. Listen and check.

CD2 14

PRONUNCIATION

1 *Alice in Wonderland* was written by Lewis Carroll.

2 There were two wrong answers in the exam.

3 *The Sword in the Stone* was written in 1938.

4 The woman twisted her wrist twice.

5 William ate two whole watermelons.

4 Work with a partner. Read and answer. Ask and answer.

1 What's your favourite film?

___

2 When was it released?

___

3 What's it about?

___

4 Who are the main characters played by?

___

5 Why do you like it?

___

For more grammar practice go to page 105.

Which is the odd one out? Why? written / draw / made / created

4 Lesson 5 **Vocabulary, Reading and Writing**

1 Read and write the words in the puzzle.

1 This is a person who records sound in a studio.
2 This is a person who takes photographs as a job.
3 This is a person who tells people how to perform.
4 This is a person who writes music.
5 This is a person who invents and writes stories.
6 This is a person who performs in a film or a play.
7 This is a person who creates new styles of clothes.
8 This is a person who paints on walls in public places.

2 Match the children with a job. There are four extra jobs.

fashion designer   musician   novelist   photographer   actor   sound engineer   film director   composer

1 **Matt:** My favourite hobby is listening to music. I'm crazy about pop music! I love writing songs in my free time, but I can't play a musical instrument. In the future I'd love to work with performers in a studio.

____

2 **Jill:** I love sewing and I think I'm really good at sketching, too. In the future I'd like to do a job creating things with different fabrics.

____

3 **Mia:** I'd like to have a creative job when I'm older. I love the theatre and watching films. However, I'm also quite shy so I don't think I'd like to work in front of a camera.

____

4 **Harry:** I enjoy creative activities, but I can't draw or paint very well. I've got a great imagination and I love scaring people with the horror stories I write.

____

3 Read and learn.

Word building

When we write a definition we often use these relative pronouns:

It's a person *who / that* …
It's a place *where* …
It's something *which / that* …

4 Complete the definitions. Use a relative pronoun.

1 An artist is ____________________
2 An art gallery is ____________________
3 Clay is ____________________
4 A theatre is ____________________
5 A stage is ____________________
6 A sculptor is ____________________

Which is the odd one out? Why? studio / painter / sculptor / actor

After you read

1 Read the definitions and find the words in the comic strip.

1 This adjective means without the other thing in a pair. ___odd___
2 These are things which are scary but not real. ______________
3 This action happens when somebody takes people away as prisoners. ______________
4 This is a light, cool material which is used to make clothes. ______________
5 This is something that we can't explain. ______________
6 This is a soft toy made from clothing. ______________

2 Complete the comic strip frames.

3 Listen and complete the advert. CD2 17 Exams Practice

Comic drawing competition

Topic: (1) ______________

Rules: Comics must have (2) ______________ frames.

There mustn't be any (3) ______________ or weapons.

Place and date: the town library on Saturday at (4) ______________

Age groups: age 8 to 12, age 13 to (5) ______________

Prizes: 1st prize: a set of comic books and (6) ______________
2nd and 3rd prize: a new art set

4 Write about a comic strip you know. Ask and answer.

1 Who or what is the main character? ______________
2 What's the main character like? ______________
3 What's your opinion of the comic strip? ______________

Which is the odd one out? Why? novel / comic book / comic strip / graphic novel

Develop your writing skills

1 Add a full stop, a question mark or an exclamation mark. Then write two more sentences.

1 That picnic looks delicious

2 Can I have a sandwich, please

3 Be careful, Jane

4 ______________________________________.

5 ______________________________________!

Plan your writing

2 Cooperative learning Work with a partner. Plan your comic strip. Make notes.

1 Who are the characters? ______________________________

2 What happens in:

Frame 1: ______________________________

Frame 2: ______________________________

Frame 3: ______________________________

Frame 4: ______________________________

Frame 5: ______________________________

Frame 6: ______________________________

3 Which sound effects do you need? ______________________________

3 Now write the six frames of your comic strip in your notebook. Remember to include full stops, question marks and exclamation marks.

4 Learning to learn Read your comic strip to a new partner. Then check your work together. Put a tick (✓) or a cross (✗).

The comic strip is easy to understand. ☐

I've used captions to explain the story. ☐

It's clear who is speaking or thinking. ☐

I've included sound effects. ☐

The sentences finish with correct punctuation. ☐

It's enjoyable to read. ☐

Which is the odd one out? Why? speech bubble / caption / exclamation / chapter

1 Complete the conversations. Use expressions to give praise. Act out.

1 Guess what! I've won a prize for a short story. ______

2 I've just finished my drawing. Look! ______

3 I learnt to play the drums last year. ______

4 I'm going to sing in a concert tomorrow. ______

Prepare a conversation

2 Thinking skills Make notes about your creative activities.

Creative me!

Creative activities I do:
______
______
______

Objects and materials I use:
______
______
______

The best creative things I've done:
______
______
______

Creative activities I'd like to try:
______
______
______

3 Write questions to ask a partner.

1 *Do you enjoy doing creative activities?*

2 ______

3 ______

4 ______

5 ______

Have a conversation

4 Talk with your partner about your creative activities.

Remember! Praise people when they tell you about an achievement.

My progress

5 Reflect on the unit Read and complete the sentences.

In this unit I've learnt about ______

In this unit I've learnt to ______

I think that my work in Unit 4 is ______

The ways I can improve are ______

Which is the odd one out? Why? the middle / the top / the corner / the background

Cooperative learning Work with a partner to do the quiz.

1 Write the verbs.

1 ______________ a film
2 ______________ ceramics
3 ______________ origami
4 ______________ jewellery
5 ______________ an animation
6 ______________ a play

2 Write the sentences. Use the past passive.

~~*Avatar*~~ Jack Sparrow Donald Duck *Diary of a Wimpy Kid*

create direct play write

Walt Disney Jeff Kinney Johnny Depp James Cameron

1 *Avatar* ______________________________
2 ______________________________
3 ______________________________
4 ______________________________

3 Read the answers and write the questions.

1 ______________________________? The film was made in 2010.
2 ______________________________? The photos were taken in Japan.
3 ______________________________? The poem was written by Susie.
4 ______________________________? The picture was painted in 1965.

4 Read, remember and answer the questions.

1 When was manga created?

____

2 Who was the Eiffel Tower built by?

____

3 Who was the kitten rescued by in the comic strip?

____

5 Look and order the letters. What's the mystery word?

a t i c l a m e x o n

The mystery word is: ______________________________

Definition: ______________________________

Well done. Give me five!

Using digital media creatively

1 **Sarah and Omar are talking about digital technology. Listen and number the items in the order you hear them.** CD2 19

Product Selection

0 items

digital camera

computer microphone

graphics tablet and pen

video camera

printer

mobile phone

scanner

1
laptop

2 **Listen again. What did Sarah and Omar do with the technology?** CD2 19

animation   music video   digital presentation   birthday card   digital story

1 Sarah used a laptop to create a ______________.

2 Sarah used a digital camera to create an ______________.

3 Omar used a graphics tablet and a printer to create a ______________.

4 Omar used a scanner and a microphone to create a ______________.

5 Omar used a video camera to create a ______________.

3 **Read and answer the questions about digital technology.**

1 Which digital technology have you used?

____

2 What did you create with this technology?

____

3 What technology haven't you used?

____

4 What would you like to create in the future?

____

4 **Work with a partner. Ask and answer the questions in Activity 3. Are your answers the same?**

I've used a video camera to make a video about sport.

I've used a laptop to find information about space.

Unit 5 Write it down!

1 Find and circle the words. Complete the chart.

J	Z	S	Q	M	G	T	R	Q	A	J	F	V	B	J
S	E	Z	A	P	R	I	E	I	S	V	Z	L	S	Y
Z	E	J	Q	K	E	U	G	L	Z	M	O	J	H	R
H	M	N	O	T	E	K	E	M	F	G	E	B	L	E
R	X	W	L	R	T	T	F	X	P	A	S	F	L	V
F	T	J	M	D	I	E	D	O	M	T	E	I	F	C
C	R	F	W	H	N	L	S	T	N	P	A	L	G	D
G	E	T	Z	U	G	T	Y	T	V	M	X	V	U	N
E	V	X	V	A	S	G	T	N	E	Q	F	K	D	H
F	D	B	N	J	C	P	E	O	D	M	Y	A	R	N
C	A	C	F	W	A	R	W	Q	L	J	N	O	O	A
A	N	S	O	F	R	A	C	B	M	E	Z	H	S	C
W	X	Z	Z	K	D	A	Y	L	A	C	X	F	B	L

Messages on paper	Messages not on paper	Both
leaflet		

2 Read and complete the definitions.

1 ________________: This is a language used by people who can't hear. People use their hands to communicate.

2 ________________: This is an instant message system that allows you to communicate using the Internet.

3 ________________: This is a piece of paper that is usually free and gives information about something.

4 ________________: This is a type of story that has drawings and words. It's usually funny.

5 Greetings card: ________________

6 Text message: ________________

3 Read and remember the grammar in the lesson.

Which language **does** *flamingo* **come from**? It **comes from** Portuguese.
Where **does** Lionel Messi **come from**? He **comes from** Argentina.

4 Write the question and the answer.

1 Which language does *giraffe* come from? ________________

2 ________________ He comes from Spain.

Which is the odd one out? Why? book / newspaper / brochure / TV

1 Read and write. Use *said* or *told*.

Reported speech

1 The teacher ___told___ me I was doing very well.
2 Pedro ________ he wanted a cheese sandwich.
3 Jake ________ his mum he wasn't feeling very well.
4 Sally ________ her friend she didn't understand Italian.
5 They ________ the film was really good.
6 I ________ I didn't like ice cream very much.

2 Complete the sentences. Use reported speech.

1 'I understand sign language.' Harry told me he ________
2 'I'm writing all the information for you.' The teacher said she ________
3 'My sister's going to the cinema tonight.' Hannah said her sister ________
4 'I want to play tennis this evening.' Matthew told me he ________

3 Listen and complete the notes.

CD2 23 Exams Practice

The school book club

Day: (1) ________

Time: (2) ________ to 1pm

Place: (3) ________

How long: We choose one book to read in (4) ________ weeks.

What we are reading now: *The Secret Language* by (5) ________.

What we do: We talk about the books, we have quizzes or we (6) ________ of the scenes and characters.

4 Read and answer. Ask and answer.

1 When do you read? ________
2 What kinds of books do you read? ________
3 Is there a book club at your school? When does it meet? ________
4 Which book would you like to read at a book club? ________

Which is the odd one out? Why? page / DVD / cover / ink

After you read

1 Remember the information. Read and answer the questions.

1 Where was the Rosetta Stone discovered? It ______
2 What was on the Rosetta Stone? There ______
3 Where was Jean-Francois Champollion from? He ______
4 What did Champollion promise himself? He ______
5 What does the Egyptian word *ra* mean? It ______
6 What happened after Champollion told his brother the news? He ______

2 Listen and complete the notes. Write one, two or three words each time.

CD2 25

Cracking the code

1 The story is about ______ hieroglyphics.
2 Tom ______ of the Rosetta Stone.
3 Callum thinks the symbols on the hieroglyphics are ______.
4 Tom and Jess have got ______.
5 Callum's favourite part is when Champollion is so ______ that he faints.
6 Callum thinks that he ______ their code.

3 Thinking skills What do you think of the information?

I think ______.

I give it ______ stars. ☆☆☆☆☆

4 Find out about Egypt with your family. ICT

1 In which two seas can you swim in Egypt? ______
2 What's the name of the longest river in the world? ______
3 What's the Great Sphinx of Giza? ______
4 How many sides have the Egyptian Pyramids got? ______
5 What's papyrus? What was it used for? ______

Which is the odd one out? Why? king / pharaoh / emperor / soldier

Reported speech with *will* / *would* & *can* / *could*

1 Read and circle the correct pronoun.

1 Jason told *I* / *me* he wouldn't come to my house today.
2 My parents said *they* / *them* would come and watch the match.
3 Henry said *he* / *him* was hungry.
4 You told me *she* / *her* could swim really well, didn't you?
5 Kenny told *they* / *them* he was playing basketball.

2 Complete the sentences. Use reported speech.

1 'We won't go to the museum in the morning.' Julia said they wouldn't go to the museum in the morning.
2 'I can swim to the other side of the pool.' Alex told me he ______
3 'I can't play the guitar as well as Joseph.' Dan said he ______
4 'I'm sorry but I can't help you.' Kelly told me she ______
5 'We'll watch the film tomorrow.' Harry told me they ______

3 Listen and complete the sentences. When is *would* contracted?

CD2 28

PRONUNCIATION

1 James said he ______ meet me at lunchtime.
2 Jenny told her friend she ______ going to the concert.
3 Mrs Jones told the children they ______ go and play outside.
4 My grandad always said he ______ play chess, but he just beat me!
5 I said I ______ play my music very loudly.
6 They said they ______ come to the party on Saturday.

4 Work with a partner. Ask your partner questions about their plans for this evening. Write the answers.

me

1 Liam said he wouldn't do his homework this evening.
2 ______
3 ______
4 ______
5 ______

Will you do your homework this evening?

No, I won't.

For more grammar practice go to page 106.

Which is the odd one out? Why? would / could / can / was

1 Read and complete the definitions.

1 The text that describes a photo or an illustration is called a ______.

2 The part of a magazine or website that talks about clothes and style is called the ______.

3 An ______ is when someone asks another person questions about themselves.

4 The first page of a newspaper is called the ______.

5 The title of a newspaper article is called a ______.

2 Read the text and the questions. Circle A, B, C or D. Exams Practice

Welcome to *Film Focus*. Today, Evie tells us what she thought of *Out in Space*.

Out in Space tells the story of four astronauts. Their spaceship gets lost and they lose communication with Earth. We watch their adventures as they try to find a way to return to Earth.

I thought it started very slowly but soon I was completely hooked. I couldn't wait to find out how they would get home.

The acting was fantastic! Janine Walton was especially good. Her character gets braver as the film goes on and Walton showed that in an excellent way. There wasn't very much music. I think that music can make dramatic moments even more exciting, but there was a lot of silence in the film.

The best part was the special effects. They were awesome. At one point there was a spectacular crash. I don't know how they made that look so life-like!

So, I'd recommend this film. It's a bit long, but it's worth it!

1 What's the writer doing in this text?
A Giving her opinion about a film she's seen.
B Giving information about different films about space.
C Suggesting how actors can improve.
D Telling us how to survive if things go wrong in space.

2 What does Evie think about the film?
A There was too much music in the film.
B The acting wasn't very good.
C It was exciting although not from the start.
D She knew what was going to happen at the end.

3 What do you think 'hooked' means?
A bored
B enjoying something very much
C comfortable
D surprised

4 What might Evie say about the film?
A 'The most impressive thing was the special effects.'
B 'I wish it were a bit longer.'
C 'The women were much better than the men.'
D 'It was very loud.'

3 Read and learn.

Word building

Some adjectives end in *-ed* and others in *-ing*.

What's the difference in meaning?
I was *surprised*.
The end of the film was *surprising*.

4 Read and circle the correct adjectives.

1 I didn't like the film at all. I thought it was *boring* / *bored*.

2 The match is about to start. I'm so *exciting* / *excited*!

3 I was really *surprising* / *surprised* at how good the acting was.

4 The beginning of the book was very *exciting* / *excited*, but it got less interesting after that.

5 I didn't know anyone at the party so I was *boring* / *bored*.

Which is the odd one out? Why? exciting / interesting / boring / amazing

After you read

1 Read and write *A* (right), *B* (wrong) or *C* (doesn't say).

1 Computer coding is more popular in schools than football. ☐
2 The coding club at Chippington Primary School started three years ago. ☐
3 There are three volunteer teachers who help at coding club. ☐
4 The same children go to coding club each week. ☐
5 The other teachers in the school are learning, too. ☐
6 The school would like to have more volunteers to help teach coding. ☐

2 Read the definitions and find the words in the text.

skills generation ~~keep up with~~ animations volunteers programmers

1 This means to stay at the same level as someone else. *keep up with*
2 These are people who can use codes to make websites. ______
3 These are people who do something without receiving money. ______
4 This is all the people in a group who were born at a similar time. ______
5 These are abilities people have, usually because of experience or training. ______
6 These are short films that show something moving. They use pictures. ______

3 Listen to the interview and order the questions. Listen again and answer the questions.

CD2 31

When did you start going to coding club? ☐ ______
Is programming animations easy? ☐ ______
Do you have any other hobbies? ☐ ______
What do you enjoy most about it? ☐ ______
How old are you? 1 ______
What job would you like to do when you grow up? ☐ ______

4 Cooperative learning Work with a partner. Write two more questions. Act out the interview.

______

______

Which is the odd one out? Why? keyboard / mouse / plate / screen

Develop your writing skills

1 Read and complete the sentences. Use *so*.

1 Rosie doesn't like ice cream *so she decided to have fruit instead.*

2 The door was locked ______

3 James really likes sport ______

4 The forest was dark and quiet ______

5 Gemma didn't think she was going to get a prize ______

6 It was raining while Mr Cookham was cycling home ______

Plan your writing

2 Cooperative learning Work with a partner. Plan your newspaper article. Make notes.

1 Who's the story about? ______

2 What did they do? ______

3 When did it happen? ______

4 Where did it happen? ______

5 What's the title? ______

6 What's the first sentence? ______

______

7 What information will you include at the end of the article? ______

______

3 Now write your newspaper article in your notebook. Remember to use direct and reported speech.

4 Learning to learn Read your text to a new partner. Then check your work together. Put a tick (✓) or a cross (✗).

My newspaper article's got a good title.	☐
I've included a sentence to introduce the news story.	☐
I've included reported speech in my newspaper article.	☐
I've included direct speech in my newspaper article.	☐
The events are written in a clear order.	☐
There's a reference for people to get more information.	☐

Which is the odd one out? Why? article / question / report / review

1 Order the conversation. Then act out.

Have you ever met a famous person?	1	He came to our school once, about a year ago.	
Wow! Your school? Was he friendly?		Yes, he was. He was friendly and funny, too.	
Really? How did you meet him?		He told some brilliant stories about working in films. We laughed a lot!	
Why was he funny?		I'm not sure. Let me think. Yes! John Carter, the film star.	

Prepare a conversation

2 Thinking skills Make notes about meeting a famous person.

The time I met ______

How it happened:
______
______
______

What they were like:
______
______
______

What they said:
______
______
______

How you felt:
______
______
______

3 Write questions to ask a partner.

1 *What was he / she like?*
2 ______
3 ______
4 ______
5 ______

Have a conversation

4 Talk with your partner about meeting a famous person.

Remember! Use some phrases to give you time to think about your answers.

My progress

5 Reflect on the unit Read and complete the sentences.

In this unit I've learnt about ______
In this unit I've learnt to ______
I think that my work in Unit 5 is ______
The ways I can improve are ______

Which is the odd one out? Why? reporter / doctor / comedian / notebook

Cooperative learning Work with a partner to do the quiz.

1 Complete the words.

1 bl ___ g p ___ st 3 l ___ ___ fl ___ t 5 ch ___ t m ___ ss ___ g ___ 7 c ___ rt ___ ___ n

2 br ___ ch ___ r ___ 4 n ___ t ___ 6 gr ___ ___ t ___ ngs c ___ rd 8 ___ m ___ ___ l

2 Look and write the correct word.

1 ____________________ page

2 ____________________

3 ____________________

4 ____________________

3 Read and complete the sentences. Use reported speech.

My name's Ben. I live in Australia. My family are fans of AFC Ajax, a great football team. I play football and cricket every Saturday.

1 He said ______________________________ Ben.

2 He said ______________________________ in Australia.

3 He said his ______________________________ AFC Ajax.

4 He said he ______________________________ every Saturday.

4 Write the correct verbs in the chart.

Direct speech		Reported speech	Direct speech		Reported speech
are	→	*were*	go	→	________
can	→	________	is	→	________
will	→	________	have to	→	________
wear	→	________	fall	→	________

5 Read, remember and answer the questions.

1 What kind of club did you read a newspaper article about? ______________________________

2 What does the school ask for at the end of the article? ______________________________

6 Look and order the letters. What's the mystery word?

b a d y e o k r

The mystery word is: ______________________________

Definition: ______________________________

Well done. Give me five!

Using digital media to research and present information

1 Listen to the conversation. Tick the information that the children learn in Hungarian. CD2 33

- the word for 'strawberry' ☐
- the word for 'cat' ☐
- the word for 'elephant' ☐
- the word for 'horse' ☐
- how to say 'hello' ☐
- how to say 'goodbye' ☐
- how to say 'yes' ☐
- how to say 'no' ☐
- how to count from one to five ☐
- how to pronounce the letters 'sz' ☐
- how to pronounce the letters 'cz' ☐
- how to pronounce the letter 'k' ☐

2 Listen again and answer the questions. CD2 33

1 What does 'macska' mean in English? ________
2 How do you write 'no' in Hungarian? ________
3 What is an accent? ________
4 What does 'szia' mean in Hungarian? ________

3 Cooperative learning Work in pairs. Choose a language to research and complete the notes below.

Choose some vocabulary, e.g. animals, colours, food, parts of the body: ________

In English	In ________	In English	In ________
________	________	________	________
________	________	________	________

How to say 'hello' and 'goodbye': ________

How to count from 1 to 5: ________

How to say 'yes' and 'no': ________

How to pronounce some of the letters: ________

Are there any accents? ________

4 Work with another pair who chose a different language. Present all your information to the class. Use different digital technology.

The word for 'Hello' in Spanish is 'Hola'.

The word for 'Hello' in Turkish is 'Selam'.

Unit 6 Our future

1 Find and circle the words. Write.

①

②

③

P	E	D	E	T	E	C	T	I	V	E	T	I
A	L	U	J	Y	A	J	F	V	T	N	C	V
X	E	U	T	F	E	V	E	L	O	Z	A	W
T	C	G	M	E	B	J	W	Y	U	E	H	W
W	T	T	R	B	O	Q	D	S	R	B	M	W
A	R	C	H	A	E	O	L	O	G	I	S	T
V	I	Z	Y	R	W	R	R	V	U	Q	S	G
F	C	N	D	E	F	K	V	B	I	N	R	W
U	I	H	B	C	M	L	A	A	D	I	D	M
A	A	D	K	S	N	M	D	I	E	O	Y	G
V	N	U	N	G	E	I	N	S	R	G	M	N
N	A	I	C	I	T	I	L	O	P	E	E	P

④

⑤

⑥

1 politician
2 ______
3 ______
4 ______
5 ______
6 ______

2 Read and complete the definitions.

1 A ______ is a person who helps a vet to look after sick and injured animals.
2 A ______ is a person who protects objects, buildings and workers.
3 A ______ is a person who designs pictures and text for magazines, adverts, books and newspapers.
4 A ______ is a person who installs, repairs and makes sure computers work correctly.
5 A businessperson ______
6 A physiotherapist ______

3 Read and remember the grammar.

A vet **has to** have a degree. A vet **doesn't have to** work at night.

4 Describe a job. Use *have to* or *don't have to*. Read the sentences to a partner. Can your partner guess the job?

1 (uniform) You ______
2 (tools) ______
3 (work outside) ______
4 (good at) ______

Which is the odd one out? Why? tour guide / politician / detective / vet

Making predictions about the future

1 Read and circle the correct option.

1 Matt (may) / *won't* be a musician because he loves playing the drums.
2 Sue *will* / *could* be an engineer because she's studying engineering.
3 Lucy *will* / *may* be a detective because she loves reading mystery stories.
4 Sara *might* / *won't* be a graphic designer because she loves ICT.
5 Tim *may* / *won't* be a tour guide because he loves travelling.
6 Harry *will* / *won't* be an archaeologist because he isn't interested in history.

2 Make predictions for you. Use *will, may, might, could* or *won't*.

1 (tour guide) I ______________________________
2 (plumber) ______________________________
3 (veterinary nurse) ______________________________
4 (politician) ______________________________
5 (security guard) ______________________________

3 Listen and circle YES or NO. CD2 37 Exams Practice

Plans for the weekend

1	Jake might go to the cinema on Saturday.	**YES**	**NO**
2	Jake may see his grandparents on Sunday.	**YES**	**NO**
3	Vicky will probably go shopping with her mum on Saturday.	**YES**	**NO**
4	Vicky will definitely go to the beach on Sunday.	**YES**	**NO**
5	Vicky may watch TV on Sunday.	**YES**	**NO**

4 Write about your plans for the weekend. Tell your partner.

1 I'll probably ______________________________
2 I definitely won't ______________________________
3 I may ______________________________
4 I ______________________________
5 I ______________________________

Which is the odd one out? Why? may / might / could / won't

After you read

1 Remember the story. Read and answer the questions.

1 When did Evelyn start to learn the piano? When ______
2 Why did she begin to play percussion instruments? Because ______
3 Which parts of the body did she use to feel a drum's vibrations? She ______
4 What happened when Evelyn was 19? She ______
5 How did she achieve her dream? She ______
6 Why does the text say that 'there are no limits for Evelyn'? Because ______

2 Listen and complete the notes. Write one, two or three words each time.

CD3 1

The story of Evelyn Glennie

1 This true story is about a famous ______.
2 Tom is surprised to learn that Evelyn ______.
3 Jess saw Evelyn ______ once.
4 Jess's favourite instrument was made from ______.
5 Jess would like to go ______.
6 Jess is going to recommend the story to ______.

3 Thinking skills What do you think of the story?

I think ______.
I give it ______ stars. ☆☆☆☆☆

4 Find out about Scotland with your family. ICT

1 What's the capital of Scotland? ______
2 What's Scotland's highest mountain? ______
3 What's haggis? ______
4 What is 'Nessie'? Where does it live? ______
5 What are bagpipes? ______

Which is the odd one out? Why? drum / guitar / triangle / cymbals

Embedded questions

1 Order and write the embedded questions. Ask and answer.

1 Do / will / you / watch / tonight / you / think / TV? *Do you think you will watch TV tonight?*
2 be / you / famous / will / Do / you / think? ____________________
3 you / tonight / have / Do / will / think / you / pizza? ____________________
4 you / Do / you / a / be / will / think / detective? ____________________

2 Complete the sentences.

1 (1 hour) I might go to the park *in one hour's time.*
2 (10 minutes) This class will finish ____________________
3 (3 months) The weather will be hotter ____________________
4 (1 year) I'll go to another school ____________________
5 (3 years) I won't drive a car ____________________
6 (30 seconds) The bell will ring ____________________

3 Read and draw the intonation pattern. Listen and check.

CD3 4

PRONUNCIATION

1 I'll wear glasses next year.
2 He may speak French in 10 years' time.
3 They'll probably go home in one hour's time.
4 She could wear glasses in two years' time.
5 I might study English in 20 years' time.
6 I won't do my homework tonight.

4 Read and answer. Use the time reference *in … 's time* or *in … s' time*. Ask and answer.

1 When will you be fourteen? ____________________
2 When will you go home? ____________________
3 When will you go to bed? ____________________
4 When will you leave school? ____________________
5 When will you have a job? ____________________

For more grammar practice go to page 107.

Which is the odd one out? Why? last year / next week / tomorrow / later

1 Look and write the actions.

1 ____________________

2 ____________________

3 ____________________

4 ____________________

5 ____________________

6 ____________________

7 ____________________

8 ____________________

2 Read and circle A, B, C or D. Exams Practice

Children and their future

More (1) ______________ 3,000 children in Europe have participated in a survey to find (2) ______________ how young people see the future. (3) ______________ of the children predict that there'll be lots of new technology, like robots and flying cars, and this technology will help us live longer and (4) ______________. The most popular wish is to live in a world without war and crime. (5) ______________, ten per cent of the children (6) ______________ a job that is fun and well paid when they are older.

	A	B	C	D
1	that	what	of	than
2	up	in	out	down
3	Most	More	Any	One
4	best	worse	worst	better
5	Last	Then	Too	Finally
6	like	ask	want	hope

3 Read and learn.

Word building

Sequencing words can help us remember new vocabulary:

infant school → primary school → secondary school → university

4 Look at Activity 1. In which order will you do these things? Use *definitely, probably, might* or *could*.

1 First, I'll probably ____________________

2 Then, ____________________

3 ____________________

4 ____________________

5 Finally, ____________________

Which is the odd one out? Why? college / university / office / school

After you read

1 Read the letter again and order the information.

The writer's signature	☐	A greeting to the reader	☐
The address and the date	1	An introduction to the time capsule	☐
The writer's predictions for the future	☐	The writer's closing message	☐
A description of the writer's daily life	☐	The writer's wishes for the future	☐

2 Read the definitions and find the words in the text.

1 This is a small round container where you can keep things. *capsule*

2 This is a small electronic device that you use to make calculations. ____________

3 These are flat pieces of plastic that have got tape inside for playing sound. ____________

4 These are large electronic games in a room or building. ____________

5 These are large places where products like cars are made. ____________

6 This is a treatment that makes an ill person better. ____________

3 Listen and complete the notes.

CD3 7 Exams Practice

The New York World's Fair time capsule

The time capsule was buried in (1) ____________.

The time capsule will be buried for (2) ____________ years.

The outside of the capsule is made of (3) ____________ and the inside is made of (4) ____________.

There is a mechanical car and a (5) ____________ inside the time capsule.

Another object in the capsule is some (6) ____________.

4 Which objects would you put in a time capsule? Why?

1 I would put ____________ because ____________

2 ____________

3 ____________

4 ____________

Which is the odd one out? Why? doll / bike / building blocks / computer game

Develop your writing skills

1 Read the letter again and find examples of the following. Write and order.

1 A greeting: ______ ☐
2 A closing message: ______ ☐
3 How the writer introduces himself: ______ ☐
4 Information included in the body of the message: ______ ☐
5 A prediction for the future: ______ ☐
6 The writer's address: ______ ☐

Plan your writing

2 Cooperative learning Work with a partner. Plan your letter. Make notes.

1 Where is your time capsule buried? ______
2 A greeting: ______
3 Your daily routines: ______
4 Your favourite possessions: ______
5 Your predictions for the future: ______
______
6 Your wishes for the future: ______
______
7 A closing message: ______
______

3 Now write your letter in your notebook. Use your notes in Activity 2 to help you. Remember to organise the information into paragraphs.

4 Learning to learn Read your letter to a new partner. Then check your work together. Put a tick (✓) or a cross (✗).

The address is in the top right corner. ☐
The date is below the address. ☐
The letter starts with a greeting. ☐
There's new information in each paragraph. ☐
I've included a closing message. ☐
It's interesting to read. ☐

Which is the odd one out? Why? address / date / signature / heading

1 Order the conversation. Act out.

Because they look after people who are ill.	☐	They sometimes give injections.	☐
Why not?	☐	A nurse! Why's that?	☐
I'd like to be a nurse when I'm older.	1	Because I'm scared of injections.	☐
I wouldn't like to do that.	☐	That's a good reason. What else do they do?	☐

Prepare a conversation

2 Thinking skills Make notes about a job you'd like to do in the future.

A job I'd like to do ____________

What workers do in this job:
____
____
____

Skills and qualities you need in this job:
____
____
____

Why I like this job:
____
____

Advantages of this job:
____
____

Disadvantages of this job:
____
____

3 Write questions to ask a partner.

1 *What job would you like to do in the future?*
2 ____________
3 ____________
4 ____________
5 ____________

Have a conversation

4 Talk with your partner about a job you'd like to do.

Remember! You can use the expression *What else?* to find out more information.

My progress

5 Reflect on the unit Read and complete the sentences.

In this unit I've learnt about ____________
In this unit I've learnt to ____________
I think that my work in Unit 6 is ____________
The ways I can improve are ____________

Which is the odd one out? Why? photograph / painting / picture / film

Cooperative learning Work with a partner to do the quiz.

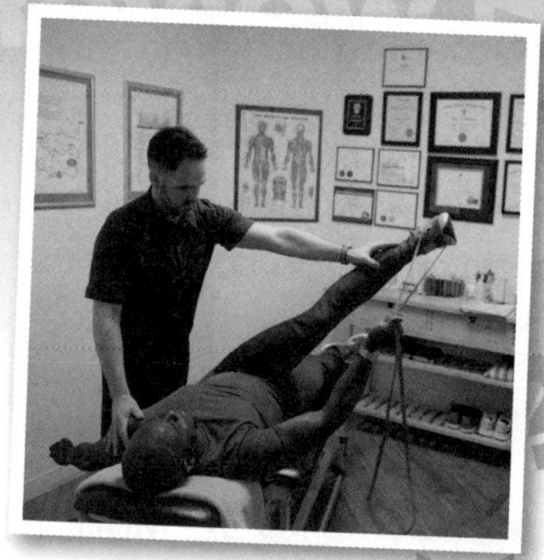

1 Read and write the words.

1 Name three jobs which need special tools:

________ ________ ________

2 Name three jobs which need a degree or a diploma:

________ ________ ________

3 Name three jobs which end in *-ian*:

________ ________ ________

2 Predict your future. Use *will, won't, may, might* or *could.*

1 (get married) I ________
2 (go to university) ________
3 (learn to drive) ________
4 (leave home) ________
5 (go backpacking) ________

3 Order and write the time expressions.

this evening in five years' time in ten years' time ~~in ten minutes' time~~ in 20 years' time the day after tomorrow next week in 11 months' time in one year's time

1 *in ten minutes' time*	4 ________	7 ________
2 ________	5 ________	8 ________
3 ________	6 ________	9 ________

4 Read and complete. Use embedded questions. Ask and answer.

1 (you / study Japanese / future) Do you think you will ________?
2 (you / watch a film / next week) ________?
3 (you / live on the moon / 20 years' time) ________?
4 (you / do all your homework / this evening) ________?

5 Look and order the letters. What's the mystery word?

n a r o a s t u t

The mystery word is: ________

Definition: ________

Well done. Give me five!

GIVE ME FIVE!

Thinking in different ways

1 **Read and listen. Circle a letter each time. Is Pedro good at thinking outside the box? Why? / Why not?** CD3 9

Are you good at thinking outside the box in a project?

1 Do you brainstorm lots of ideas at the start of the project?
- **A** Yes, always.
- **B** Sometimes.
- **C** No, I don't.

2 Do you listen to other people's ideas?
- **A** Yes, usually.
- **B** Sometimes.
- **C** No, I don't.

3 Do you like thinking of silly or funny ideas?
- **A** Yes, I love it.
- **B** Sometimes.
- **C** No, I don't.

4 Do you try to do something different from other people?
- **A** Yes, usually.
- **B** Sometimes.
- **C** No, I don't.

5 Do you ever daydream?
- **A** Yes, often.
- **B** Sometimes.
- **C** No, never.

6 Do you like solving problems?
- **A** Yes, I love it.
- **B** Sometimes.
- **C** No, I don't.

Scores A: 2 points B: 1 point C: 0 points

0–4 points: You need more practice thinking outside the box.

5–8 points: Not bad. You are quite good at thinking outside the box.

9–12 points: Well done! You are excellent at thinking outside the box.

2 **Do the quiz with a partner. Are you good at thinking outside the box in a project? Why / Why not?**

3 **Thinking skills** **Invent a robot with a partner. Read and answer the questions. Think outside the box!**

1 What useful job will your robot do? ____________________
2 How will it move? ____________________
3 What energy will your robot use? ____________________
4 How will you communicate with it? ____________________
5 What will it be called? Name your robot. ____________________
6 What will it look like? Draw your robot.

4 **Cooperative learning** **Share your ideas with another pair. Listen to their suggestions. Do you want to make any changes to your robot?**

My robot doesn't move very fast. I'll make it go faster.

Living on Mars

1 **Listen and complete the chart.** CD3 10

	Earth	Mars
Oxygen	There is oxygen in the Earth's atmosphere. People need oxygen to breathe.	__________ __________
Water	__________ __________	Nearly all of the water on Mars exists as ice and a small amount is water vapour.
Food	__________ __________	There's no life on Mars so there's no food.
Energy	The sun provides energy to help plants grow. The planet also contains fuel to create energy to help us live.	__________ __________
Ultraviolet rays	These are rays from the sun that can cause sunburn and skin cancer. Earth's atmosphere protects us from some of them.	__________ __________

2 **Cooperative learning** **Work in groups. Make notes.**

Living on Mars

Problem	Possible solutions
We can't breathe on Mars.	__________ __________ __________
We can't grow food on Mars.	__________ __________ __________
We can't keep warm and power our lives on Mars.	__________ __________ __________

1 **Cooperative learning** **Work in groups. Plan your group's home on Mars.**

Our home on Mars

The house

The structure: ______________________________

____

Inside: ______________________________

____

Food and water

____

____

Clothes

____

____

Travel

____

____

Energy

____

____

Reflect on your project

2 **Read and answer.**

1 Write three things you learnt about living on Mars.

____

____

____

2 Why were you a good group member? Write two things.

____

____

3 What could your group do better for the next project?

____

4 What mark would you give your group's work? ______ /10

Buying and selling

1 Write the words and phrases in the puzzle.

1 

2 

3 

4 

5 

6 

7 

8 

1 _ _ _ _ _ _ _ _ _

2 _ _ _ _ _ _ _

3 _ _ _ _ _ _ _ _

4 _ _ _ _ _ _

5 _ _ _ _ _ _ _

6 _ _ _ _

7 _ _ _ _ _

8 _ _ _ _ _ _ _ _ _

The mystery word is ______________________.

2 Read and complete the definitions.

1 ______________________: This is the person who wants to buy things in a shop or online.

2 ______________________: You do this when you use money to pay for something. After you do this, you have less money than you started with!

3 ______________________: This is a card made of plastic. People use it to pay for things.

4 ______________________: You do this when you keep money. You might keep it in a bank or a moneybox.

5 cashier: ______________________

6 coins: ______________________

3 Read and remember the grammar in the lesson.

This cap's **too small** for me. This shirt is **too dark**.

4 Write sentences.

expensive big loud long full ~~old~~

1 *The purse is too old.*

2 ______________________

3 ______________________

4 ______________________

5 ______________________

6 ______________________

1 

2 

3 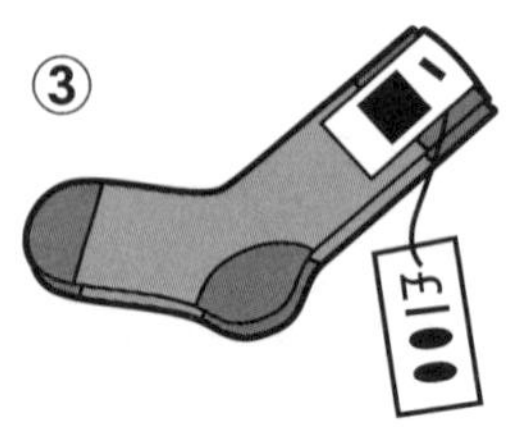

4 

5 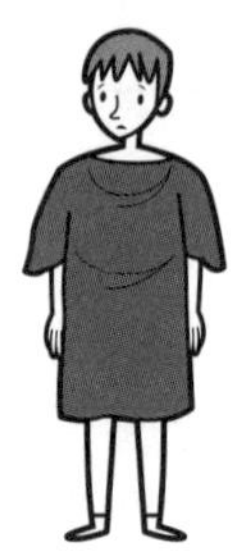

6 

Which is the odd one out? Why? moneybox / coins / banknotes / credit card

1 Read and complete the sentences. Use *too, enough* or *as*.

Comparative forms

1 This dress isn't ______________ nice as the red one.
2 Is the bag big ______________ for these books?
3 I can't see anything. It's ______________ dark.
4 I'm not tall ______________ to see the concert from here.
5 I'm not buying that. It's ______________ expensive.
6 That cashier isn't ______________ friendly as the other one.

2 Look and write sentences.

1 (as) The lemonade bottles aren't ______________________________
2 (too) It's ______________________________
3 (enough) John's new boots ______________________________
4 (too) Lauren is ______________________________

3 Listen and complete the notes.

CD3 14 Exams Practice

Sale! Books, CDs and DVDs

Day: (1) ______________

Objective: To raise (2) ______________ for local charities.

Time: (3) ______________

Place: (4) ______________

Volunteers required to (5) ______________ and also to make posters.

Bring in posters on (6) ______________.

4 Write true sentences about you or your partner.

1 (enough) ______________________________
2 (as) ______________________________
3 (too) ______________________________
4 (enough) ______________________________

Which is the odd one out? Why? tall / quickly / cheap / young

After you read

1 Remember the information. Read and answer the questions.

1 Where did Edna Ruth Byler go in 1946? She ____________________

2 Why did she want to help people there? Because ____________________

3 How did she sell the materials? She ____________________

4 How long did Edna continue to work with craftspeople? She ____________________

5 What kinds of foods do the farmers grow? They ____________________

6 How do Fair Trade organisations help the farmers? They ____________________

2 Listen and complete the notes. Write one, two or three words each time.

CD3 16

Trading fairly with others

1 This true story is about a ____________________ called Edna Ruth Byler.

2 Jess said that Edna met some ____________________ when she visited Puerto Rico in 1946.

3 Jess explained that, at first, Edna didn't sell the materials in ____________________.

4 Callum guessed that Edna ____________________ a lot of materials.

5 Callum has seen the FAIRTRADE mark ____________________.

6 Callum is going shopping this afternoon and will look out for ____________________.

3 Thinking skills What do you think of the information?

I think ____________________. I give it ____________ stars. ☆☆☆☆☆

4 Find out about the USA with your family. ICT

1 What's the capital city of the USA? ____________________

2 Which state is the largest and also the coldest? ____________________

3 What's the second most spoken language in the USA? ____________________

4 How many points are on the Statue of Liberty's crown? ____________________

5 Where's the Gateway Arch and what does it look like? ____________________

Which is the odd one out? Why? save / pay / buy / spend

First conditional

1 Read and circle the correct form.

1 If it *will rain* / *rains* on Sunday, we *won't play* / *play* baseball.
2 If you *will eat* / *eat* junk food every day, you *won't be* / *aren't* healthy.
3 Maisie *won't win* / *wins* the race if she *will run* / *runs* so slowly.
4 Mum *will take* / *takes* us to the cinema if we *will help* / *help* her tidy the house.
5 If I *sell* / *will sell* all the food, I *will go* / *go* and get some more.

2 Complete the questions.

1 What ___will you do___ (you do) if there ___aren't___ (not be) any tickets left?
2 What ______ (happen) if you ______ (go) to the supermarket without any money?
3 What ______ (you do) if the shirt ______ (be) too big?
4 What ______ (your mum say) if she ______ (see) that your moneybox is empty?
5 What ______ (you do) if you ______ (not find) your receipt?

3 Listen and complete the sentences. Listen again and circle the sounds that are linked.

CD3 20

PRONUNCIATION

1 If you don't ______ me the answer, I'll get really upset.
2 I don't believe you. You always tell ______.
3 I really like the way the poster looks. It has a really good ______.
4 I love listening to calm ______.
5 My cousin ______ loses at table tennis. She's amazing.

4 Work with a partner. Ask and answer.

1 What will you do if it's sunny on Saturday?
If it's sunny on Saturday, I'll go to the swimming pool with my friends.
2 What will you do if it rains on Saturday?
______
3 What will you eat if you go to a restaurant tomorrow?
______
4 What will you see if you go to the cinema on Sunday?
______

For more grammar practice go to page 108.

Which is the odd one out? Why? cap / sun cream / umbrella / sunglasses

1 Look and write sentences.

1 *The wheel is loose.* ______
2 ______
3 ______
4 ______

2 Read the text and the questions. Circle A, B, C or D.

Exams Practice

Plate-smashing in Greece

If you go to a Greek restaurant or a Greek wedding, you will no longer see people throwing and breaking plates, a fun tradition that stopped many years ago. This isn't because plates are expensive though; breaking plates can be dangerous and many people have been hurt.

But how did this tradition start? In ancient Greece, people smashed plates at funerals to remember the dead. The ancient Greeks also believed that by smashing plates, bad luck wouldn't come into their homes and only good luck would follow.

As the years passed, people started smashing plates at weddings. This was done to wish the new couple good luck and wealth. In restaurants where there was live music, plate-smashing became popular because it was a symbol of good fun and wealth.

If you go to a wedding now, you will see people throwing flowers and rice, which is just as fun. In restaurants people no longer throw plates, but the food is still as delicious as it was in the past.

1 What's the writer doing in this text?
A Giving information about a tradition that started in Greece.
B Encouraging people to visit Greece.
C Giving advice about the dangers of plate-smashing.
D Explaining the differences between Greek weddings and other weddings around the world.

2 What did some people think?
A That plate-smashing is a recent tradition.
B That plate-smashing stopped because it was expensive.
C That plate-smashing didn't hurt anyone.
D That plate-smashing should only happen in restaurants.

3 Why did people smash plates in ancient Greece?
A To hurt other people.
B To stop bad luck coming into their homes.
C To celebrate weddings.
D To bring wealth.

4 What does the writer think about Greek restaurants?
A It's expensive to throw rice in them.
B People should throw flowers in them.
C They are just as enjoyable as before.
D The food has got worse.

3 Read and learn.

Word building

Many adjectives end in *-y, -ous, -ful.*

For example: *messy, mysterious, cheerful.*

4 Think and write more adjectives.

-y

messy ______ ______

-ous

dangerous ______ ______

-ful

cheerful ______ ______

Which is the odd one out? Why? smash / crash / loud / bang

After you read

1 Read the adverts again and correct the sentences.

1 You have to push yourself along with your feet when you use the Tiger Waveboard.

____

2 You don't receive anything extra when you buy the Swoop Stunt Kite.

____

3 You can only use the Splash 500 boat in calm lakes.

____

4 The Tiger Waveboard is not suitable for teenagers.

____

5 The adverts tell us that the Splash 500 and the Tiger Waveboards are easy to use.

____

2 Complete the sentences. Use *so*.

1 The Swoop Stunt Kite is light *so it's easy to carry it around.*

2 The Splash 500 is made of tough plastic ______________________________

3 There's a special offer on the Splash 500 boats ______________________________

4 It takes minutes to learn to use the Tiger Waveboard ______________________________

5 The Swoop Stunt Kite's sail is made of strong polyester ______________________________

3 Listen and complete the information.

CD3 24 Exams Practice

SUMMER SALE

Merton Sports Shop, 135 (1) ____________ Street.
Hundreds of great offers! Sale must end on (2) ____________.
(3) ____________ and T-shirts are half-price.
We have even got trainers for under (4) ____________ euros.
Only 50 pairs, so hurry!
Late opening until (5) ____________ on Thursdays.
Free raffle tickets for all customers. First prize is a (6) ____________.

4 Thinking skills Which of these offers would you most like to try? Why?

Three bars of chocolate for the price of two!

Buy one pair of trainers and get the second pair free!

All children's books half-price!

Which is the odd one out? Why? fibreglass / polyester / plastic / discount

Develop your writing skills

1 Write slogans for these products. Use alliteration, rhyme or both.

①

②
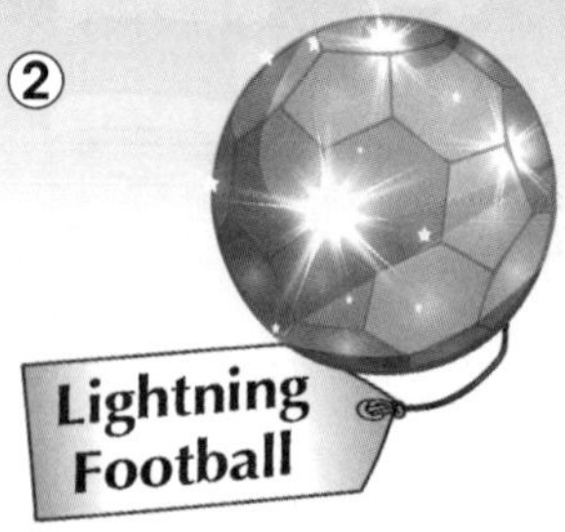

③

④

1 ______________________________

2 ______________________________

3 ______________________________

4 ______________________________

Plan your writing

2 Cooperative learning Work with a partner. Plan your advert. Make notes.

1 What kind of product is it? ______________________________

2 What's it called? ______________________________

3 What adjectives will you use to describe the product? ______________________________

4 Quote from a famous person you'll include: ______________________________

5 Which questions will you use to raise interest? ______________________________

____

6 What are the best things about the product? ______________________________

7 A slogan you'll include: ______________________________

3 Now write your advert in your notebook. Remember to use alliteration and rhyme.

4 Learning to learn Read your advert to a new partner. Then check your work together. Put a tick (✓) or a cross (✗).

I've included a quote from a famous person. ☐

I've included questions to raise interest. ☐

There's a description of the product. ☐

I've managed to get the reader to imagine having the product. ☐

I've used alliteration and rhyme in my slogan. ☐

I've said how good the price is. ☐

Which is the odd one out? Why? amazing / comfortable / sensational / fantastic

1 Order the conversation. Act out.

Do your parents give you pocket money? [1]

What are you saving up for? [ ]

Do you always spend it? [ ]

I spend money on computer games, too! [ ]

I want to buy some new books and computer games. [ ]

Yes, they do. I get £15 a month. [ ]

No, I don't. I save most of it. [ ]

Prepare a conversation

2 Thinking skills Make notes about money.

Money

Pocket money:

______

______

______

Saving money:

______

______

______

Spending money:

______

______

______

Other:

______

______

______

3 Write questions to ask a partner.

1 *What do you spend your money on?*

2 ______

3 ______

4 ______

5 ______

Have a conversation

4 Talk with your partner about money.

Remember! Don't just answer yes or no. Give details or examples.

My progress

5 Reflect on the unit Read and complete the sentences.

In this unit I've learnt about ______

In this unit I've learnt to ______

I think that my work in Unit 7 is ______

The ways I can improve are ______

Which is the odd one out? Why? bank / supermarket / bookshop / chemist's

Cooperative learning Work with a partner to do the quiz.

1 Complete the words.

1 c__sh__ __r
3 pr__c__ t__g
5 s__v__ m__n__y
7 c__st__m__r
2 p__rs__
4 t__ll
6 m__n__yb__x
8 c__ __ns

2 Imagine you are returning four different things to a shop. Write sentences. Use the adjectives.

cracked stained bent ripped

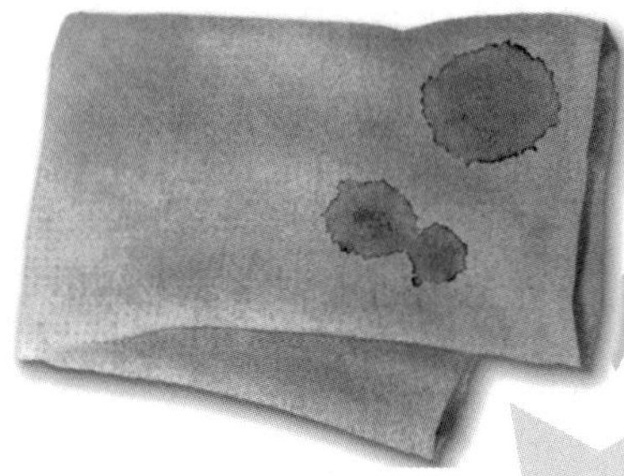

1 ______________________________
2 ______________________________
3 ______________________________
4 ______________________________

3 Complete the sentences for you.

1 We're too young ______________________________
2 We're not strong enough ______________________________
3 Our class is not as ______________________________
4 We're not small enough ______________________________

4 Complete the sentences. Use the first conditional.

1 If it rains all day, we'll ______________________________
2 If my class wins the competition, ______________________________
3 If you do exercise every day, ______________________________
4 If my friend comes to my house this evening, ______________________________
5 If we miss the bus, ______________________________

5 Read, remember and answer the questions.

1 What three objects were advertised in this unit? ______________________________
2 What do we call the text which is used to sell an object? ______________________________

6 Look and order the letters. What's the mystery word?

p t e i c r e

The mystery word is: ______________________________

Definition: ______________________________

Well done. Give me five!

Initiative and entrepreneurial skills

1 Listen to the conversation. Complete the information. CD3 26

	Price	The children choose (✓)
Mangoes	£12.00 for 1 kilogram	☐
Raspberries	______ for 1 kilogram	☐
Strawberries	______ for 1 kilogram	☐
Peaches	______ for 1 kilogram	☐
Vanilla ice cream	______	☐
Raspberry ice cream	£8.00	☐

What price will each smoothie be? __________

2 Listen again and answer the questions. CD3 26

1 How much will the ingredients cost? __________

2 How much money will they have if they sell all the smoothies? __________

3 Do you think they have made good decisions? Why / Why not? ______________________________

____

3 Cooperative learning Work in pairs. Decide what smoothies to make and what the price will be.

	Price	
Mangoes	£12.00 for 1 kilogram	☐
Apples	£9.00 for 1 kilogram	☐
Raspberries	£8.00 for 1 kilogram	☐
Strawberries	£6.00 for 1 kilogram	☐
Pears	£5.00 for 1 kilogram	☐
Vanilla ice cream	£4.00	☐
Strawberry ice cream	£8.00	☐
Chocolate ice cream	£5.00	☐

What price will each smoothie be? __________

Language bank

… is too expensive.

I think … and … are good together.

It costs … for a kilogram.

Let's buy …

Shall we buy … ?

How much have we spent?

Let's sell them for …

4 Show your smoothie idea to another pair. Is theirs similar? Tell them good things about their idea and things they can improve.

Your smoothie looks great but it's a little too sweet.

Your smoothie is delicious but it is a little too expensive.

Unit 8 Let's dream

1 Order and write the words from the lesson.

lamp eter — 1 ____________________

lacro — 2 ____________________

ase nilo — 3 ____________________

horse — 4 ____________________

tinag ritesoto — 5 ____________________

policart sihf — 6 ____________________

2 Read and complete the definitions.

1 ____________________: You do this activity under the sea. You breathe oxygen through a tube.

2 ____________________: You usually do this in the daytime. You close your eyes and have a short sleep.

3 ____________________: You do this activity in a small boat. You paddle the boat on the sea.

4 ____________________: This is a type of bed made with a long piece of cloth. It is tied between two trees.

5 Boogie boarding: ____________________

6 Wildlife spotting: ____________________

3 Read and remember the grammar in the lesson.

Would you **like to** go scuba diving? Yes, I **would**. **Would** you **like to** swim with a shark? No, I **wouldn't**.

4 Read and answer the questions. Ask and answer.

1 Would you like to be famous? Why? / Why not? ____________________

2 Would you like to visit a different country? Why? / Why not? ____________________

3 Would you like to learn another language? If so, which? ____________________

4 Would you like to live in a different country? If so, which? ____________________

5 Would you like to have a pet tarantula? Why? / Why not? ____________________

Which is the odd one out? Why? scuba diving / sailing / surfing / sea kayaking

Second conditional

1 Read and circle.

1 If I *live* / *lived* in England, I'd *speak* / *spoke* English every day.
2 I wouldn't *swim* / *swam* in the sea if I *live* / *lived* in Alaska.
3 I'd *see* / *saw* kangaroos if I *live* / *lived* in Australia.
4 If I *see* / *saw* a giant tortoise, I'*d be* / *was* happy.
5 I'*d feel* / *felt* tired if I *hike* / *hiked* to the top of a volcano.
6 If I *go* / *went* kayaking, I'*d wear* / *wore* a life vest.

2 Read and complete. Use the second conditional.

1 If I ___lived___ (live) in France, I'd ___speak___ (speak) French.
2 I wouldn't ________ (get) tired if I ________ (climb) a volcano.
3 I'd ________ (see) tropical fish if I ________ (swim) in the Galapagos Islands.
4 I'd ________ (take) lots of photos if I ________ (see) a giant tortoise.
5 I'd ________ (have) a nap if I ________ (feel) tired.
6 If I ________ (see) an iguana, I wouldn't ________ (touch) it.

3 Listen and circle A or B. CD3 30 Exams Practice

The Galapagos Islands	YES	NO
1 Michelle would go snorkelling if she visited the Galapagos Islands.	A	B
2 Michelle would be afraid if she saw an iguana in the water.	A	B
3 If Joe travelled by boat, he'd feel seasick.	A	B
4 If Michelle saw a giant tortoise, she'd take lots of photos.	A	B
5 If Joe walked through the lava tunnel, he'd take a rope.	A	B

4 Read and answer. Ask and answer.

1 Which activity would you do if you visited the Galapagos Islands?

If I visited the Galapagos Islands, I ________________

2 What would you take if you visited the Galapagos Islands?

If ________________

3 How would you feel if you swam next to a small shark?

If ________________

Which is the odd one out? Why? kangaroo / giant tortoise / iguana / sea lion

After you read

1 Remember the story. Read and answer the questions.

1 What was the yacht called? It ______
2 What attacked the yacht? A ______
3 How many lifeboats did the couple have? They ______
4 Why didn't the ships see the lifeboats? Because ______
5 How long were the couple in the lifeboats? They ______
6 Who finally rescued the couple? A ______

2 Listen and complete the notes. Write one, two or three words each time.

CD3 32 Exams Practice

A dream trip

1 This true story is about a couple who wanted to sail to ______.
2 Callum said it took the couple ______ to reach the Pacific Ocean.
3 Callum's favourite moment in the story was when a ______ attacked the yacht.
4 Callum said it was interesting to find out what the couple ______ in the lifeboats.
5 The part Callum didn't like was when the ______.
6 Callum wouldn't recommend this story to ______.

3 Thinking skills What do you think of the story?

I think ______. I give it ______ stars. ☆☆☆☆☆

4 Find out about Ecuador with your family. ICT

1 What's the capital of Ecuador? ______
2 Which line goes through Ecuador? ______
3 What's Cotopaxi? ______
4 How many islands make up the Galapagos Islands? ______
5 How were the islands formed? ______

Which is the odd one out? Why? rope / wings / sail / compass

Second conditional questions

1 Complete the questions. Ask and answer.

1 Would you _be_ (be) scared if you ________ (see) a snake?
2 Would you ________ (cry) if you ________ (cut) your finger?
3 Would you ________ (feel) happy if you ________ (meet) a film star?
4 Would you ________ (eat) fish and chips if you ________ (visit) London?
5 Would you ________ (remember) your friends if you ________ (be) famous?
6 Would you ________ (go) skiing if you ________ (live) in Canada?

2 Write the questions. Ask and answer.

1 What / do / if / win a lot of money? _What would you do if you won a lot of money?_
2 What / do / if / get lost? ________
3 How / feel / if / lose your bag? ________
4 Where / go / if / visit Paris? ________
5 Where / live / if / be a famous person? ________

3 Listen and write the missing words. Which sentences have the contracted form of *would*? Listen and repeat.

CD3 35

PRONUNCIATION

1 I _'d_ visit the museum.
2 _They_ play golf in the afternoon.
3 ________ swim with dolphins.
4 ________ read a guide book.
5 ________ go to the library.
6 ________ catch a cold.
7 ________ take my camera.
8 ________ study hard.

4 Write questions about imaginary situations. Ask and answer.

What would you do if you found a gold ring in the street?

If I found a gold ring, I'd give it to the police.

1 What would you do if you found ________?
2 What would you do if you met ________?
3 ________
4 ________

For more grammar practice go to page 109.

Which is the odd one out? Why? found / lost / met / opened

1 Write the missing letters. Tick (✓) three things you'd like to do.

1 w___n th___ l___tt___ry ☐
2 h___v___ thr___ ___ w___sh___s ☐
3 ___ ___t ___ ___ ___ ___t ☐
4 tr___v___l b___ck ___n t___m___ ☐
5 b___ ___nv___s___bl___ ☐
6 b___ th___ pr___s___d___nt ☐
7 tr___v___l ___n sp___c___ ☐
8 m___ ___t ___ f___m___ ___ ___s p___rs___n ☐

2 Read the text and the sentences. Write *A* (right) or *B* (wrong).

Where would you go?

A few years ago, a children's website in Britain asked the question 'Where would you go if you could travel anywhere in the world?' Almost all of the children said that they'd travel abroad. Favourite destinations included Australia and the Caribbean because of their fantastic beaches. Some children said that they'd love to visit a capital city and see a famous monument like the Eiffel Tower or the Statue of Liberty, and others wanted to see the South American rainforests. Finally, a few of the children said they wanted to go to parts of the world that were poorer or that had wars so that they could help the people in those places. What about you? Where would you go if you could travel anywhere in the world?

1 Most of the children wanted to visit a place close to their home. ☐
2 The most popular destinations were places with beaches. ☐
3 Some of the children wanted to visit a big city. ☐
4 All of the children wanted to have a good time. ☐

3 Read and learn.

Word building

We often use *anyone, anything* or *anywhere* after *if* in a conditional sentence. For example:

Where would you go if you could travel *anywhere* in the world?

Who would you like to meet if you could meet *anyone* in the world?

What would you change if you could change *anything* in the world?

4 Work with a partner. Look at the *Word building* box and write the answers. Ask and answer.

1 If I could travel anywhere in the world, I'd ______________________________
____

2 ______________________________
____
____

3 ______________________________
____
____

Which is the odd one out? Why? someone / no one / somewhere / anyone

After you read

1 Read and order the events.

I explored the jungle.	☐	I found a bag.	☐
I found food and drink.	☐	I built a shelter.	☐
There was an explosion.	☐	I made friends with a monkey.	☐
I was sailing on a ship.	1	I woke up on a beach.	☐
I banged my head.	☐	I looked for my friends.	5

2 Read and answer the questions.

1 How does the writer feel at the end of the first day?

The writer ______________________________

2 How would you feel if you woke up on a desert island?

If I ______________________________

3 What did the writer eat on the second day?

____

4 What would you eat if you were on a desert island?

____

3 Listen and circle A, B or C.

CD3 38 Exams Practice

Diary of a Wimpy Kid

1 What kind of school does Greg go to?

A He goes to a junior school.

B He goes to a middle school.

C He goes to a senior school.

2 Where did the Wimpy Kid first appear?

A He appeared in a novel.

B He appeared in a film.

C He appeared on a website.

3 What else can the author do?

A He can design web pages.

B He can design computer games.

C He can play computer games.

4 How long did it take to write the first book?

A It took one year.

B It took five years.

C It took nine years.

4 Whose diary would you like to read? Why? Ask and answer.

a pop star's diary | a footballer's diary | an explorer's diary | a friend's diary

Which is the odd one out? Why? palm tree / monkey / jungle / polar bear

Develop your writing skills

1 Complete the sentences.

I we Our My mine ~~ours~~ me ours

1 We built this hut. It's ___ours___.

2 The coconut hit ______ on my head and ______ felt dizzy.

3 ______ boat sank and now ______ are on a desert island.

4 All the island is ______. I'm the king of this island!

5 ______ friends were on the boat and I don't know where they are.

6 Hands off! This map is ______. We found it.

Plan your writing

2 Cooperative learning Work with a partner. Plan your diary extract. Make notes.

Day 10

1 What happened? ______

2 What did you do? ______

3 What did you see? ______

4 How did you feel? ______

5 A personal reflection: ______

3 Now write your diary extract in your notebook. Use your notes in Activity 2 to help you. Remember to use the first person.

4 Learning to learn Read your diary extract to a new partner. Then check your work together. Put a tick (✓) or a cross (✗).

- I've included the day or date. ☐
- I've used the first person. ☐
- I've written the events in order. ☐
- My diary extract includes interesting information. ☐
- I've described my feelings. ☐
- My diary extract includes a reflection. ☐

Which is the odd one out? Why? its / me / my / mine

1 Answer the questions. Use different expressions to say when you're not sure. Ask and answer.

1 Do you think you will travel a lot in the future? ____________________

2 Would you like to travel in time? ____________________

3 Would you like to live in another country? ____________________

4 Do you think you will be famous? ____________________

Prepare a conversation

2 Thinking skills Make notes about time travel.

Time travel

How far and where I'd travel to:

____

____

____

What I would see:

____

____

____

What I would do:

____

____

____

What I would bring back:

____

____

____

3 Write questions to ask a partner.

1 *Would you travel to the past or the future?*

2 ____________________

3 ____________________

4 ____________________

5 ____________________

Have a conversation

4 Talk with your partner about time travel.

Remember! It's OK to say you're not sure if someone asks you a question.

My progress

5 Reflect on the unit Read and complete the sentences.

In this unit I've learnt about ____________________

In this unit I've learnt to ____________________

I think that my work in Unit 8 is ____________________

The ways I can improve are ____________________

Which is the odd one out? Why? wood / forest / statue / lake

Cooperative learning Work with a partner to do the quiz.

1 Look and write the words.

1 *palm tree*

2 ____________

3 ____________

4 ____________

5 ____________

6 ____________

2 What would you do if you lived in the Galapagos Islands? Write sentences.

1 If ____________

2 ____________

3 ____________

3 Complete the sentences. Use the second conditional.

1 If I were two metres tall, ____________

2 I'd be happy ____________

3 If I could meet anyone, ____________

4 Read and complete the questions.

Jess: What ____________?

Callum: I'd help people if I were the president.

Jess: ____________?

Callum: I'd go to Canada if I travelled abroad.

5 Read, remember and answer.

1 How did the whale attack the yacht in the story? ____________

2 How did the writer begin each diary extract? ____________

6 Look and order the letters. What's the mystery word?

s c o p a m s

The mystery word is: ____________

Definition: ____________

Well done. Give me five!

Working as a team

1 **What tips does Zoe give Amal? Listen and tick (✓).** CD3 40

1. Make sure that everyone participates. ☐
2. Ask for other people's opinion. ☐
3. Take turns to speak. ☐
4. Make sure you listen to what other people say. ☐
5. Try to look and sound friendly. ☐
6. Be open to new ideas. ☐

2 **Cooperative learning** **Work in a group of three. Read the instructions. Discuss and choose.**

You are lost on a **desert island**. Talk together about the different objects and **choose five** to help you survive.

compass

penknife

toilet roll

mirror

matches

island map

bottle of water

life jacket

Language bank

What do you think about taking …?

I think the … is / are a good idea because …

The … isn't / aren't a good idea because …

I'm not so sure.

That's a good point.

I agree / disagree.

Our group has chosen: ______________________

3 **Explain your list to another group. Is their list the same or different? Do you want to change your list?**

4 **Thinking skills** **Think about how you worked together as a group. Look at the tips in Activity 1. What did you do well? What can you do better?**

Unit 9 School: past and future

1 **What do you use in your school? Complete the diagram. Add three more items you know.**

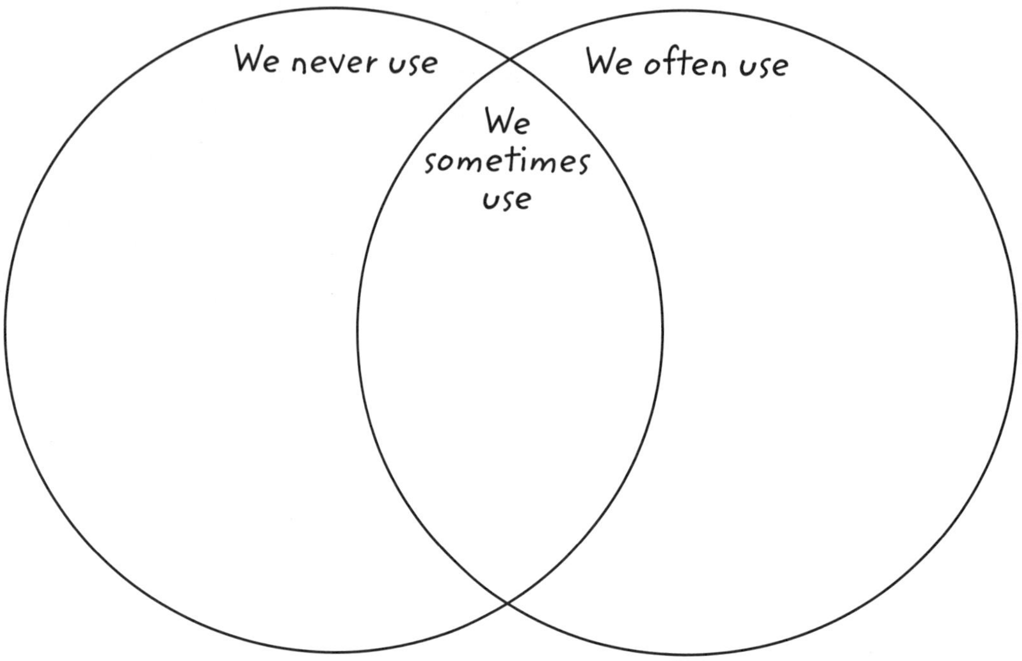

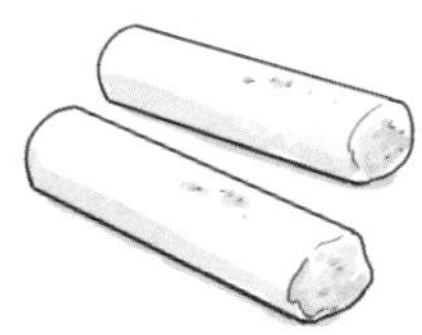

2 **Read and complete the definitions.**

1 ______________________: This is a piece of clothing that you wear on top of your normal clothes. It keeps your normal clothes clean when you work.

2 ______________________: This is a strong piece of fabric. It's usually rectangular and you paint on it with oil paints.

3 ______________________: This is a straight line of chairs or desks. You can see these in a classroom or a cinema.

4 ______________________: This is a piece of soft rock which is used for writing on a blackboard.

5 blackboard: ______________________

6 laboratory: ______________________

3 **Read and remember the grammar in the lesson.**

How long have you lived in your town? I've lived here **for** two years. / I've lived here **since** I was ten.

4 **Read and answer. Ask and answer.**

1 How long have you studied English? ______________________

2 How long have you studied at this school? ______________________

3 How long have you known your teacher? ______________________

Which is the odd one out? Why? calculator / paintbrush / canvas / oil paints

Past habits: *used to*

1 Read and complete. Use *used to* or *didn't use to.*

walk have ~~use~~ punish be work

1 Teachers *didn't use to use* interactive whiteboards in the past.
2 Most children ______________________ to school fifty years ago.
3 Teachers ______________________ a lot stricter.
4 Children ______________________ in silence in the past.
5 Children ______________________ laptops forty years ago.
6 Teachers ______________________ pupils a lot more in the past.

2 Write the questions. Ask and answer.

1 (go to infant school / two) *Did you use to go to infant school when you were two?*
2 (use a computer / four) ______________________
3 (have English classes / five) ______________________
4 (wear an overall / six) ______________________
5 (do homework / eight) ______________________

3 Listen and complete. Write one, two or three words.

CD4 2 Exams Practice

School rules in the past

Pupils had to (1) ______________________ when they answered a question.

Pupils weren't allowed to (2) ______________________.

Pupils who were (3) ______________________ were punished.

Girls had to do (4) ______________________ and boys had to do technical (5) ______________________.

Pupils had to use their (6) ______________________ to write.

4 Thinking skills Work with a partner. Do you think schools were better in the past? Write.

I think ______________________ because ______________________

____

____

____

Which is the odd one out? Why? slate / laptop / chalk / blackboard

9 Lesson 3 **Culture around the world: Sweden**

After you read

1 Remember the story. Read and answer the questions.

1 When was Alfred Nobel born? He ______

2 What did he create when he moved back to Sweden? He ______

3 Where was his obituary published? It ______

4 How did he feel when he read his obituary? He ______

5 What did he decide to do with his money? He ______

6 What does Malala want for all the children in the world? She ______

2 Listen and complete the notes. Write one, two or three words each time.

CD4 4 Exams Practice

The Nobel Prizes

1 Tom thought the story was ______.

2 Tom said that Alfred Nobel was ______ of dynamite.

3 Callum thought that there were only ______ Nobel prizes.

4 The sixth prize is for progress in ______.

5 Tom thinks that the ______ is the most important.

6 Malala wrote ______ to tell the world her story.

3 Thinking skills What do you think of the story?

I think ______. I give it ______ stars. ☆☆☆☆☆

4 Find out about Sweden with your family. ICT

1 Which countries have a land border with Sweden? ______

2 What colours are the Swedish flag? ______

3 Which country is connected to Sweden by a bridge? ______

4 What currency does Sweden use? ______

5 What's a moose? ______

Which is the odd one out? Why? medicine / chemistry / peace / art

Future: *going to* & *will*

1 Read the sentences. Decide if each sentence is a *plan, prediction* or *decision.*

1 I'm going to learn French. ___*plan*___
2 I'll switch on the heater. ______
3 He'll pass the exam. ______
4 I'll do my homework now. ______
5 We're going to have a party. ______
6 My team will definitely win the match. ______

2 Complete the sentences. Use *will* or *going to.*

1 I think that my class ______ (pass) the exam.
2 It's my birthday tomorrow so I ______ (have) a party.
3 I'm sorry, I forgot. I ______ (tidy up) my room now.
4 Do you think you ______ (be) a famous pop star?
5 I ______ (watch) my favourite TV series at 6.

3 Listen and write the number of words you hear. Listen again and write the sentence.

CD4 7

PRONUNCIATION

1 [6] *Where are you going to go?*
2 [ ] ______
3 [ ] ______
4 [ ] ______
5 [ ] ______

4 Read and answer. Ask and answer.

1 What are you going to do after school today? ______
2 What do you think schools will be like in the future? ______
3 What subjects are you going to study next year? ______
4 If there's a class party at the end of the term, what will you bring? ______
5 Where do you think you'll live in the future? ______

For more grammar practice go to page 110.

Which is the odd one out? Why? next week / now / in a minute / tomorrow

1 Look and write the words.

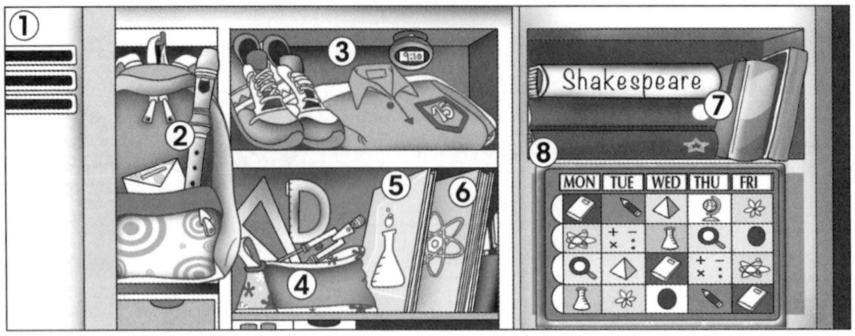

1 locker
2 ______
3 ______
4 ______
5 ______
6 ______
7 ______
8 ______

2 Read and circle A, B, C or D. Exams Practice

Life at a football academy

Do you know that there are special schools (1) ______ train young football players? They are called academies and they are always looking (2) ______ new football talent. Life at an academy is exciting, (3) ______ it's hard work, too. You must train three times a week after your normal school day and you also (4) ______ to practise at home. Then, at the weekend (5) ______ are matches against other teams. Football academies aren't for (6) ______, but if your dream is to become a professional football player, they could be the perfect place for you.

	A	B	C	D
1	where	that	than	who
2	for	after	up	at
3	so	although	but	because
4	must	need	should	needn't
5	their	there	they're	they
6	everyone	someone	no one	anyone

3 Read and learn.

Word building

Some nouns in English are made with two separate words. These are called **compound nouns**.

For example: *sports kit, classroom, timetable, geometry set.*

4 Put the words together to make compound nouns.

~~lap~~ oil book heart milk secondary home head

work phones ~~top~~ paints shelf break school shake

1 laptop
2 ______
3 ______
4 ______
5 ______
6 ______
7 ______
8 ______

Which is the odd one out? Why? Chemistry / Literature / Physics / Biology

After you read

1 Read and circle the correct word.

1 *Worried from Liverpool* is going to a new school in *August / September / October.*

2 *Worried from Liverpool*'s mum says that it's silly to feel *nervous / shy / worried.*

3 Fran says that all the new classmates will feel *different / the same / excited.*

4 Fran suggests doing a/an *after-school / weekend / lunchtime* activity.

5 Fran thinks it's a good idea to keep in touch with *new friends / old friends / teachers.*

2 Work with a partner. Read the advice and say what the problem is.

1 Why don't you study a bit longer every day?

2 What about taking drawing lessons?

3 Try to repeat the words you hear twice.

4 You could take a nap.

3 Read the problem and write the advice. Compare with your partner.

1 I haven't got any money. Advice: ____________________

2 I'm really hungry. Advice: ____________________

3 I'd like to make more friends. Advice: ____________________

4 I'm always late for school. Advice: ____________________

4 Listen and circle A, B or C.

CD4 10

Agony Aunt

How to prepare for exams

1 What is Tim worried about?
- A his exams
- B his homework
- C his marks

2 How should Tim revise?
- A for long periods of time
- B for periods of 15 minutes
- C for short periods of time

3 What does Tim need to do the night before?
- A revise a lot and go to bed late
- B revise a little and go to bed early
- C relax and go to bed early

4 What does Tim need to remember?
- A the day and time of the exam
- B to take the correct equipment
- C to enjoy the exam

5 Thinking skills Work with a partner. Think of a problem and write a conversation in your notebook. Act out.

What's the matter?

I feel terrible …

Which is the odd one out? Why? university / secondary school / college / sports centre

Develop your writing skills

1 Read and match the sentence halves.

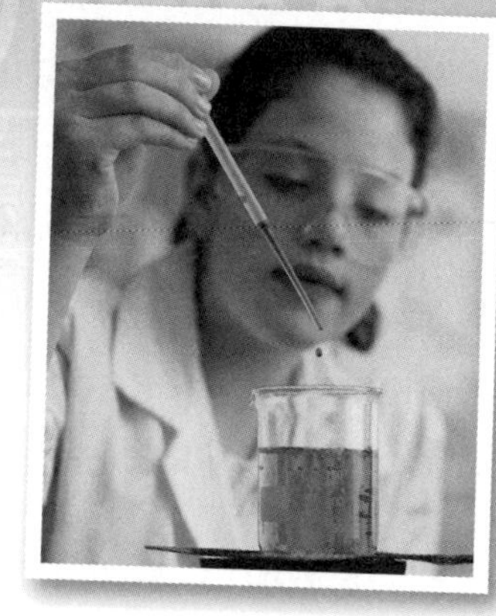

1 I'm shy so	*e*	a	I'll enjoy Physics and Chemistry.
2 I think I'll lose my books because	☐	b	I know I'll get lost.
3 I love science so	☐	c	I'm very untidy.
4 The school is really big so	☐	d	there are lots of after-school clubs.
5 I'll have to work hard because	☐	e	it will be difficult to make new friends.
6 I won't be bored because	☐	f	there's more homework.

Plan your writing

2 Cooperative learning Work with a partner. Plan your advice. Make notes.

1 Choose a problem to answer:

I'm worried about doing exams. ☐ I'm worried about some bullies. ☐

I can't go to sleep at night. ☐ Other: ____________________

2 The receiver's name: ____________________

3 A kind comment you'll make: ____________________

____

4 Two suggestions: ____________________

____

5 Give a choice: ____________________

6 A positive ending: ____________________

____

3 Now write your advice in your notebook. Remember to include an opening and closing message.

4 Learning to learn Read your advice to a new partner. Then check your work together. Put a tick (✓) or a cross (✗).

I've chosen a problem to answer.	☐
I've included an invented name.	☐
I've made some suggestions.	☐
I've given the person I'm writing to a choice.	☐
The advice sounds friendly and sympathetic.	☐
The ending sounds positive.	☐

Which is the odd one out? Why? excited / nervous / worried / afraid

1 Read and complete the explanations.

1 It's something you wear when ______ I know. It's a sports kit.

2 ______ You mean chalk.

3 ______ That person's called a teacher.

4 ______ Ah! You mean the laboratory.

Prepare a conversation

2 Thinking skills Make notes about education.

Education

What I used to do at nursery school:

What I do at primary school:

What I'm going to do at secondary school:

What I want to do after secondary school:

3 Write questions to ask a partner.

1 What was nursery school like?

2 ______

3 ______

4 ______

5 ______

Have a conversation

4 Talk with your partner about education.

Remember! Explain a word if you don't know it in English.

My progress

5 Reflect on the unit Read and complete the sentences.

In this unit I've learnt about ______

In this unit I've learnt to ______

I think that my work in Unit 9 is ______

The ways I can improve are ______

Which is the odd one out? Why? snorkel / goggles / ropes / towel

Cooperative learning Work with a partner to do the quiz.

1 Read and write the words.

1 Three materials for painting: ____ ____ ____
2 Three kinds of technology in schools: ____ ____ ____
3 Three things you can wear in school: ____ ____ ____
4 Three secondary school subjects: ____ ____ ____

2 Thinking skills Think about when you were six years old. Answer.

1 What did you use to wear for school? I used to ____
2 What did you use to play at break time? ____
3 Who did you use to play with? ____
4 What didn't you use to eat? ____
5 Where did you use to go after school? ____
6 What didn't you use to watch on TV? ____
7 What computer games did you use to play? ____

3 Write a response for each sentence. Use *will* or *going to.*

1 It's cold in here. I'll close ____
2 Why are you carrying a ball? I ____
3 This box is too heavy for me to carry. ____
4 What are your plans for the weekend? ____
5 The phone's ringing. ____
6 What are your plans for the summer? ____
7 I don't understand this activity. ____

4 Read, remember and answer.

1 What did pupils use to write on in the past? ____
2 How did Nobel use to spend his time when he was a boy? ____
3 Where's *Worried from Liverpool* going to go? ____

5 Look and order the letters. What's the mystery word?

b l e m e t i t a

The mystery word is: ____

Definition: ____

Well done. Give me five!

GIVE ME FIVE!

Managing strong feelings

1 Listen to the conversations. Tick (✓) the correct answer. CD4 12

① A What's the matter?

- [ ] Tony hasn't done his homework.
- [ ] Tony doesn't understand his homework.
- [ ] Tony has left his homework at school.

B How does Tony feel?

- [ ] angry
- [ ] worried
- [ ] embarrassed

C What advice does his dad give?

- [ ] Talk to the teacher.
- [ ] Phone a friend.
- [ ] Think about what you can do.

② A What's the matter?

- [ ] Dina can't roller skate.
- [ ] Dina can't ice skate.
- [ ] Dina can't skateboard

B How does Dina feel?

- [ ] afraid
- [ ] frustrated
- [ ] jealous

C What advice does her mum give?

- [ ] Count to ten.
- [ ] Breathe deeply.
- [ ] Think positively.

2 Thinking skills Read the situations. How would you feel?

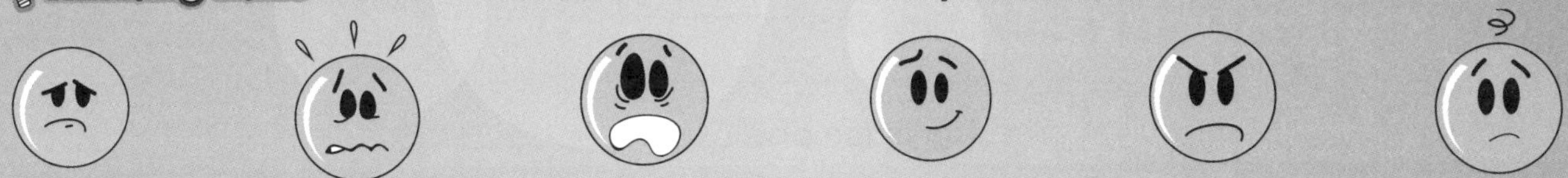

embarrassed | nervous | afraid | fine | angry | confused

1 How would you feel if you broke your new mobile phone?

I would feel ______________________.

2 How would you feel if a friend didn't invite you to a birthday party?

I ______________________.

3 How would you feel if a classmate borrowed your new pens without asking?

____

4 How would you feel if you forgot to do your homework?

____

5 How would you feel if you got lost in a park?

____

6 How would you feel if you had to sing in front of the class?

____

3 Compare your answers with a partner. Would you feel the same?

4 Thinking skills What could you do to control your emotions in Activity 2?

I could count to five before I speak when I'm angry.

Life in the past

1 **Listen and complete the chart.** CD4 13

	General information	Specific details
Playing games	1 They played on the street. 2 ______	1 The boys used to play football. 2 ______
Helping at home	1 ______	1 She used to lay the table and sweep the floor. 2 ______
Food	1 ______ 2 ______	1 The jam sponge was delicious. 2 ______
Shopping	1 They had to buy food every day.	1 They got their bread from the baker's. 2 ______

2 **Cooperative learning** **Work in groups. Write questions to ask elderly friends and relatives.**

Life in the past

Topic	Questions
School	1 ______ 2 ______ 3 ______ 4 ______
Homes	1 ______ 2 ______ 3 ______ 4 ______
Community	1 ______ 2 ______ 3 ______ 4 ______

1 **Cooperative learning** **Work in groups. Plan what you are going to put in the virtual museum.**

Life in the past

1 Our topic:

____

2 What did people use to do? (Where? / How?)

____

____

3 Which objects did people use?

____

4 Interesting information about the topic:

____

____

____

5 Things we will put in the museum (objects, photos, etc.):

____

____

____

Reflect on your project

2 **Read and answer.**

1 Write three things you learnt about life in the past.

____

____

____

2 Why were you a good group member? Write two things.

____

____

3 What could your group do better for the next project?

____

4 What mark would you give your group's work? ______ /10

Go to page 106 in your Pupil's Book.

Grammar

1 Complete the sentences. Use the past simple or the past continuous.

1 While I ______________________ (listen) to music, I ______________ (drop) my MP3 player.

2 My sister ______________ (fall off) her bike while she ________________ (ride) it in the park.

3 While we ______________________ (sleep), the wind ______________ (blow) a tree down.

4 My aunt ______________ (arrive) while I ______________________ (watch) the film.

5 It ____________________ (begin) to rain while we ________________ (have) a picnic.

2 Write the sentences. Use the past simple and the past continuous.

1 doorbell rang / while / I / watch TV

The doorbell rang while I ______________________

____

2 While the children / walk home / begin to rain

____

____

3 While Tim / swim / see a starfish

____

____

4 Sue drop a plate / while / do the washing-up

____

____

3 Read and complete the sentences. Use the infinitive or the gerund.

1 He stopped ________________ (play tennis) because it began to rain.

2 She tried ________________ (carry) the suitcase, but it was too heavy.

3 The boy promised ________________ (be) careful.

4 The tour guide suggested ________________ (visit) the museum.

4 Complete the questions. Use the infinitive or the gerund. Ask and answer.

1 Do you enjoy ______________________________?

2 Have you ever tried ______________________________?

3 Would you like to learn ______________________________?

4 Do you want ______________________________?

5 When did you start ______________________________?

6 Can you imagine ______________________________?

Vocabulary

5 Order the letters and write the definitions.

1 A *senpasger* ________________ is a person who ______________________________.

2 A *lerotly* ________________ is something that ______________________________.

3 *turparDees* ________________ is a place where ______________________________.

4 A *unrway* ______________________________

5 A *hecck-ni skde* ______________________________

6 Complete the words. Ask and answer.

1 What's a t ___ ck ___ t ___ ff ___ c ___ ?

2 What does a r ___ c ___ pt ___ ___ n ___ st do?

3 What does a b ___ ck p ___ ck ___ r do?

4 What does a g ___ ___ rd do?

5 What's a t ___ ___ r ___ st ___ nf ___ rm ___ t ___ ___ n c ___ ntr ___?

Grammar: past simple and past continuous
Vocabulary: air travel; travel and tourism

Go to page 107 in your Pupil's Book.

Grammar

1 Read and complete the questions.

1 Have you ever ____________ (meet) a famous sports person?

2 Have you ever ____________ (do) an exciting sport?

3 ______________________________ (use) a crash mat?

4 ______________________________ (go) to a football match?

5 ______________________________ (play) tug of war?

2 Read and circle the correct tense. Act out.

Jess: *Have you ever met* / *Did you meet* a famous person, Callum?

Callum: Yes, I have. I *meet* / *met* Cristiano Ronaldo last year.

Jess: Really? Where *did you meet* / *have you met* him?

Callum: I *have met* / *met* him in the airport. What about you?

Jess: Oh, no! I *didn't meet* / *haven't met* anyone famous yet.

3 Answer the questions. Use *for* or *since*.

1 How long has Emma sung in a choir? (six months)

She's sung in a choir ______________________

2 How long have your sisters played volleyball?

(they were 10) ______________________

____

3 How long has Tom made models? (last year)

____

____

4 How long have you known your best friend? (long time)

____

____

4 Ask and answer.

be at this school · know your best friend · watch your favourite programme · have your school bag · study English · live in your house / flat

Vocabulary

5 Order the letters and write the definitions.

1 A *keract* ______________ is something that ______________________________.

2 A *opoh* ______________________________

3 A *rasch tma* ______________________________

4 A *epor* ______________________________

5 A *ten* ______________________________

6 Complete the words. Ask and answer.

1 Have you ever d __ ne ph __ t __ gr __ phy?

2 Would you like to g __ t __ dr __ m __ cl __ ss?

3 Have you ever d __ ne n __ __ dl __ w __ rk?

4 Do you think m __ k __ ng m __ d __ ls is interesting?

5 Would you like to s __ ng __ n __ ch __ __ r in your free time?

Go to page 108 in your Pupil's Book.

Grammar

1 Read and circle the correct word(s).

1 There isn't *any / some* bread in the cupboard.
2 How *much / many* flour do you need to make a pizza?
3 There is *a few / a little* butter in the fridge.
4 There *is / are* a lot of garlic in this dish.
5 There aren't *much / many* sandwiches left on the plate.
6 There are *some / any* onions in this soup.
7 There aren't *any / some* tomatoes in my salad.

2 Complete the sentences. Use *to be + too much, too many* or *not enough*.

1 This cake is too sweet. There is too much sugar.
2 Oh dear! We can't make an omelette because there ______ eggs.
3 I'm sorry. There ______ chocolate for everyone.
4 There ______ tomatoes. We only need one.
5 There ______ food in the fridge. I can't close the door.
6 I prefer spicy food. There ______ chilli in this dish for me.

3 Write true sentences. Use *need to, needn't* or *mustn't*.

1 You ______ eat too many sweets.
2 You ______ eat plenty of fresh fruit.
3 You ______ do exercise every day.
4 You ______ be active.
5 You ______ stop eating chocolate.
6 You ______ drink too many fizzy drinks.

4 Ask and answer. Use *must, mustn't, should, shouldn't, need to* or *don't need to*.

I feel really tired. I've got toothache.
I've lost my mobile. I've got an exam.
I can't concentrate in class. I'm always late.

Vocabulary

5 Order the letters and write the definitions.

1 An *voacdoa* ______
2 A *mile* ______
3 *nuPatse* ______
4 A *lichil pperep* ______
5 *ricGal* ______

6 Complete the words. Ask and answer.

1 How many f __ zzy dr __ nks do you have each week?
2 How often do you eat j __ nk f __ __ d?
3 How much r __ st do you usually get?
4 How much time do you sp __ nd __ n th __ c __ mp __ t __ r?
5 How often do you d __ __ x __ rc __ s __?

Go to page 109 in your Pupil's Book.

Grammar

1 Complete the sentences. Use the past passive.

1 The play ______________________ (perform) by the children.

2 These books ______________________ (not write) by me.

3 The tower ______________________ (build) 100 years ago.

4 The portrait ______________________ (not paint) in 2013.

2 Write the sentences in the past passive.

1 Walt Disney created Donald Duck and Mickey Mouse.

Donald Duck and Mickey Mouse ______________________

____

2 Van Gogh painted *Sunflowers* in 1888.

____

____

3 James Cameron didn't direct the film *The Lord of the Rings*.

____

____

4 David Walliams didn't write *The Hunger Games*.

____

____

3 Write the questions. Use the past passive. Ask and answer.

1 Who / your favourite book / write by?

Who was ______________________

2 Where / your favourite film /make?

____

3 Where / your favourite video game / create?

____

4 Think of a verb and ask your partner. Ask and answer.

Vocabulary

5 Order the letters and write the definitions.

1 *yaCl* ______________________

2 A *getas* ______________________

3 A *stumeco* ______________________

4 *adBes* ______________________

5 A *peptup* ______________________

6 Complete the words. Ask and answer.

1 What does a f __ sh __ __ n d __ s __ gn __ r do?

2 Would you like to be a gr __ ff __ t __ __ rt __ st ? Why? / Why not?

3 What does a s __ __ nd __ ng __ n __ __ r do?

4 What do you have to do to become a n __ v __ l __ st?

5 Would you like to be a f __ lm d __ r __ ct __ r? Why? / Why not?

5 Grammar and Vocabulary Practice

Go to page 110 in your Pupil's Book.

Grammar

1 Change Tim's sentences to reported speech.

1 I love reading cartoons.

Tim said ______________________________

2 There's a note on the fridge.

Tim told me ______________________________

3 I'm writing an email to my cousin.

____

____

4 The leaflet has lots of interesting information.

____

____

2 Change Lily's sentences to reported speech.

1 Emma can speak three languages.

2 Peter will win the competition.

3 Sam won't help me.

4 I think I will pass the exam.

1 Lily said ______________________________

2 ______________________________

____

3 ______________________________

4 ______________________________

____

3 Read and circle. Act out.

Tim: I watched an interesting TV programme yesterday.

Callum: Really? What was it about?

Tim: It was about robots. A scientist *said* / *told* robots *can* / *could* speak and they *can* / *could* think now.

Callum: Wow! What else did the scientist say?

Tim: She *said* / *told* every house *will* / *would* have a robot in the future.

Callum: I hope so!

4 Play a memory game. Ask and answer.

'I can swim very well.' (Jess)
'I can remember the sentence.' (Tim)
'I've got a good memory.' (Callum)
'I won't make a mistake.' (Peter)

Vocabulary

5 Complete the words. Ask and answer.

1 Have you ever read an __ nt __ rv __ __ w in a newspaper?

2 Do you like reading the sp __ rts n __ ws?

3 Would you like to write an __ rt __ cl __ for a newspaper? What about?

4 What can you see in the f __ sh __ __ n s __ ct __ __ n of a magazine?

5 What can you see on the fr __ nt p __ g __ of a newspaper?

Go to page 111 in your Pupil's Book.

Grammar

1 Complete the sentences so they are true for you. Use *'ll definitely, 'll probably, may, might, could, probably won't* or *definitely won't*.

1 I ______________________ be a businessperson.
2 ______________________ be a computer technician.
3 ______________________ learn to drive.
4 ______________________ have lots of children.
5 ______________________ start a business.
6 ______________________ write a book.

2 Read and answer the questions. Use *in ... 's time* or *in ... s' time*.

1 When will you have your next school holiday?
I'll have my next school holiday in ______________________
2 When will you go to bed?
____
3 When will this lesson finish?
____
4 When will you be fourteen?
____

3 Write the embedded questions.

1 (think / be famous / future) Do you think you will
______________________?
2 (think / be a politician / future) ______________________
____
3 (think / fall in love / future) ______________________
____
4 (think / be a millionaire/ future) ______________________
____
5 (think / write a book / future) ______________________
____
6 (think / learn Chinese / future) ______________________
____

4 Look at Activity 3. Ask and answer.

Vocabulary

5 Order the letters and write the definitions.

1 A *icalitipon* ______________________
____
2 A *beumplr* ______________________
3 An *trecicialen* ______________________
____
4 An *charistaeogol* ______________________
____
5 A *tidteecve* ______________________
____

6 Complete the words. Ask and answer.

1 When do you think you'll l ___ ___ r n t ___ dr ___ v ___ ?
2 When do you think you'll l ___ ___ v ___ h ___ m ___ ?
3 Do you think you'll st ___ rt ___ b ___ s ___ n ___ ss in the future?
4 Do you think you'll g ___ t ___ ___ n ___ v ___ rs ___ ty? Why? / Why not?
5 Would you like to g ___ b ___ ckp ___ ck ___ ng around the world when you're older?

Go to page 112 in your Pupil's Book.

Grammar

1 Complete the sentences. Use *too* or *enough*.

expensive strong fashionable young old short

1 You can't watch that film. You aren't ______________________.
2 These trousers are ______________. I can see my ankles!
3 I'm not ______________. I can't lift this box.
4 This T-shirt is ______________. I haven't got enough money.
5 You're only twelve. That's ______________ to ride a motorbike.
6 These shoes aren't ______________. I prefer more modern ones.

2 Look and complete the sentences. Use *as + adjective + as* or *not as + adjective + as*.

£6,000	£3,000
4 years old	4 years old
Maximum speed: 120kph	Maximum speed: 120kph
5 passengers	easy to park

1 (expensive) The motorbike isn't as ______________________.
2 (old) The car is as ______________________.
3 (fast) ______________
4 (easy to park) ______________________

3 Complete the sentences. Use the first conditional.

1 If you ______________ (share) books and games, you ______________ (save) money.
2 You ______________ (save) money if you ______________ (compare) prices.
3 If you ______________ (do) some chores, you ______________ (earn) extra pocket money.
4 You ______________ (not save) money, if you ______________ (buy) lots of sweets.

4 Think of an adjective and ask your partner. Ask and answer.

Vocabulary

5 Order the letters and write the definitions.

1 A *tedcri crad* ______________
2 A *sepur* ______________
3 A *lilt* ______________
4 A *srmetocu* ______________

6 Work with your partner. Read and complete the words. Write.

1 Name three objects that can be r __ pped.
____
2 Name three objects that can be st __ __ ned.
____
3 Name three objects that can be cr __ cked.
____

Grammar: comparative forms; the first conditional
Vocabulary: money and shopping; describing damaged objects

Go to page 113 in your Pupil's Book.

Grammar

1 Complete the sentences. Use the second conditional.

1 If I ______________ (live) on a tropical island,
I ______________ (swim) every day.

2 I ______________ (take) lots of photos if
I ______________ (visit) a nature reserve.

3 I ______________ (not touch) the coral
if I ______________ (go) snorkelling.

4 If I ______________ (see) an iguana in the water,
I ______________ (not be) afraid.

5 If I ______________ (not have) any food,
I ______________ (eat) coconuts.

2 Order and write the questions.

1 be / scared / you / saw / a / Would / tarantula / you / if ? ______________

____

2 won / you / if / be / happy / a / Would / you / competition ? ______________

____

3 say / you / if / Would / hello / met / a / you / pop star ? ______________

____

4 worried / if / you / Would / you / lost / be / were ?

____

3 Complete the questions. Ask and answer.

1 What would you do if you ______________
______________?

2 How would you feel if you ______________
______________?

3 What would you say if you ______________
______________?

4 Would you ______________?

4 Work with a partner to make a chain. Use the second conditional. Act out.

If I went to London ... If I found a gold ring ...
If I travelled in space ... If I were eighteen ...
If I got lost ... If I was invisible ...

Vocabulary

5 Order the letters and write the definitions.

1 The *heors* ______________

2 A *ase olin* ______________

3 A *mochamk* ______________

4 *loCar* ______________

5 A *lapm eret* ______________

6 Complete the words. Ask and answer.

1 Where would you go if you could tr __ v __ l __ n sp __ c __?

2 Which age would you visit if you could tr __ v __ l b __ ck __ n t __ m __ ?

3 What would you do if you w __ r __ the pr __ s __ d __ nt of your country?

4 What would you buy if you w __ n th __ l __ tt __ ry?

Go to page 114 in your Pupil's Book.

Grammar

1 Write about how schools were in the past. Use *used to* or *didn't use to.*

1 The pupils used to ______

2 There didn't use to be ______

3 ______

4 ______

2 Order and write the questions. Think about when you were eight. Ask and answer.

1 to / watch / you / use / TV / What / on / did ?

______

2 use / you / What time / bed / go / to / did / to ?

______

3 songs / you / use / Which / to / did / sing ?

______

4 Which / did / listen / you / to / stories / use / to ?

______

3 Read and circle.

Tim: Hi, Callum. *I'm going to go* / *I'll go* swimming this afternoon. Do you want to come?

Callum: Not today. I have to finish my History homework. It's about schools in the past.

Tim: *I'm going to* / *I'll* help you look for information on the Internet.

Callum: Sorry, but my computer's broken. My dad *is going to* / *will* take it back to the shop tomorrow.

Tim: Don't worry. I've got my laptop in my rucksack. *I'm going to* / *I'll* use that.

Callum: Fantastic! Thanks a lot, Tim.

4 Work with your partner. Listen and offer to help.

It's very cold in this room.
I can't find my mobile phone. I'm really hungry.
The phone is ringing. It's dark in here.
I don't understand this exercise.

Vocabulary

5 Order the letters and write the definitions.

1 An *ralovel* ______

2 hkaCl ______

3 A *tolapp* ______

4 adonHephes ______

5 An *seeal* ______

6 Complete the words. Ask and answer the questions about secondary school.

1 Do you think you'll learn to play a m ___ s ___ c ___ l ___ nstr ___ m ___ nt?

2 Do you think you'll wear sp ___ rts k ___ t when you do P.E.?

3 Do you think you'll have a l ___ ck ___ r?

4 Do you think you'll use a g ___ ___ m ___ try s ___ t?

5 Do you think you'll enjoy studying L ___ t ___ r ___ t ___ r ___ ?

Grammar: past habits: *used to*; future: *going to* and *will*
Vocabulary: school equipment; secondary school

1 Read and discuss. Whole Class

1 Do you use the words *good* and *nice* when you speak and write?

2 Can you think of other words you can use that are more descriptive?

2 Complete the word web with these words. Words can go in more than one place.

delicious ~~exciting~~ beautiful kind attractive healthy confident excited entertaining tasty helpful amazing brilliant pretty

A word web

Good – Nice

A book or a film
exciting
____
____
____

What someone looks like
____
____
____

Food
____
____
____

How you feel
____
____
____

Someone's personality
____
____
____

3 In your notebook, make word webs for *bad* and *go*. What other words can you use?

4 Write these sentences again. Use other words.

1 She went to the airport and bought a good book.

____

2 Freya watched a nice film on the plane. It was better than the bad film she saw last week.

____

2 Study skills: finding out how you like learning

1 Read and discuss. Whole Class

How do you like to learn? Is there any other way of learning you would like to add to the methods below?

1 You enjoy studying the natural world.
2 You enjoy looking at graphs and designing them.
3 You enjoy performing and composing music.
4 You enjoy sport and physical activities.

2 Read the different ways people like to learn. Match them to the type of intelligence they have.

1 I enjoy doing projects on environment and nature.
2 I learn through experimenting, facts, numbers and strategy games.
3 Maps, photos and diagrams help me understand things better.
4 Role playing, physical games and performing help me learn.
5 Songs, sounds and rhythms make learning easy for me.
6 I enjoy reading and writing. I love poems, stories and reading blogs.
7 I like working in groups and helping people.
8 I keep a diary and think a lot about how I learn.

a Image Smart
b Sound Smart
c Nature Smart
d Word Smart
e Logic Smart
f Self Smart
g Body Smart
h People Smart

3 Thinking skills Think about how you like to learn. Choose the best methods for you from Activity 2. Explain why.

I'm Image Smart because photos and graphs help me learn and understand a lesson better.
I'm also People Smart because I like working in groups and sharing ideas.

4 Cooperative learning Write about how you and your partner like learning.

I am ____________________.
I like ____________________.
I don't like ____________________.

__________ is ____________________.
He / She likes ____________________.
He / She doesn't like ____________________.

1 Read and discuss.

Whole Class

1 What problems do you sometimes have with your work?

2 Does your friend have the same problems?

2 Look at the pictures and match them with the problems.

1 When the teacher gives us a test, I am often nervous.

2 When I do a test I often make mistakes.

3 When I am trying to concentrate in class, my friends sometimes talk a lot.

4 When I don't pay attention in class, I don't always understand what I need to do for homework.

5 When I do a project, my work is sometimes messy.

6 When I see something out of the window, I start to think about other things.

a  ☐

b  ☐

c 

☐

d  ☐

e  ☐

f  ☐

3 Each person wrote a plan to help themselves. Match the sentences.

EVENT

1 When I have a test on Friday, …

2 When the teacher writes our homework on the board, …

3 When I need to draw a chart, …

4 When I start to look out of the window a lot, …

5 When I write a sentence, …

ACTION

a … I will move to another desk or tell my teacher.

b … I will read it carefully before I write another sentence.

c … I will read it carefully, write it down and ask my teacher to explain it.

d … I will plan it first using a pencil.

e … I will talk to my teacher on Monday about how to study for it.

4 Think of some problems you sometimes have. How can you help yourself? Write sentences with *will* to make a plan for each problem.

Problem: ______________________________

I will ______________________________

____

____

Study skills: taking notes

1 Read and discuss. Whole Class

1 How often do you do research? Where do you do research?

2 How do you take notes? Are you good at taking notes?

2 Thinking skills Read Harry's homework. Then look at Harry's first notes from his research. What are the differences?

This week's homework: Find out about the city of New York. Write one paragraph and include five important pieces of information.

New York is the biggest and most famous city in the USA. More than eight million people live there.

Homework notes: New York

– biggest and most famous city in USA

– more than 8 million people

3 Now read the rest of Harry's notes. Choose three notes and write full sentences.

– oldest part called Manhattan

– European people arrived 500 years ago

– at beginning of 20th century, many came to find work

– people built skyscrapers – tall buildings

– big subway under city

– Central Park – very popular place – run, do sport, have picnics

1 ______________________________

2 ______________________________

3 ______________________________

4 Read the text about Sydney. Take notes in the same way as Harry.

Sydney is a big, modern city in Australia. It is the biggest city in Australia, but it is not the capital city. Today, about five million people live in Sydney. The city has many famous buildings. Sydney Opera House, which is near Sydney Harbour Bridge, opened in 1973 and is one of the 20th century's most famous buildings.

Sydney has a warm climate. It has a hot summer between December and February and is warm for the rest of the year. It is on the east coast and there are many beaches there. The most famous beach is called Bondi Beach. It is popular all through the year and people go swimming and surfing there. The Summer Olympics were held in Sydney in 2000.

5 Now use the Internet to do more research about Sydney and take notes.

Homework notes: Sydney

____

____

____

1 Look at these different ways of presenting information. Can you add more information to each one? Whole Class

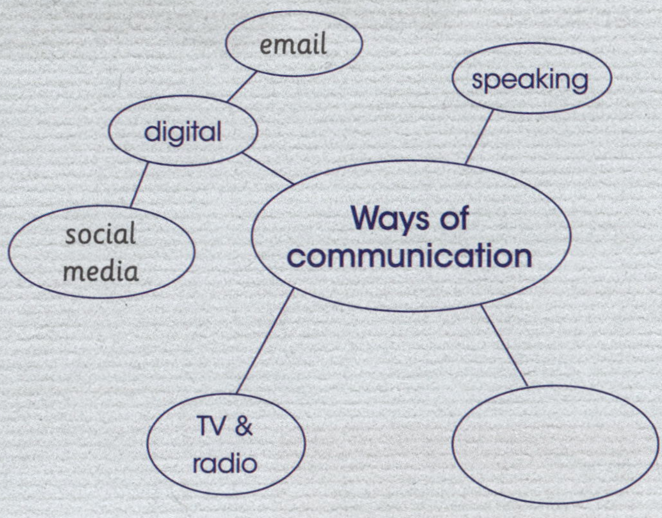

from German	from Spanish	from Arabic
hamburger	vanilla	orange
hamster		sugar

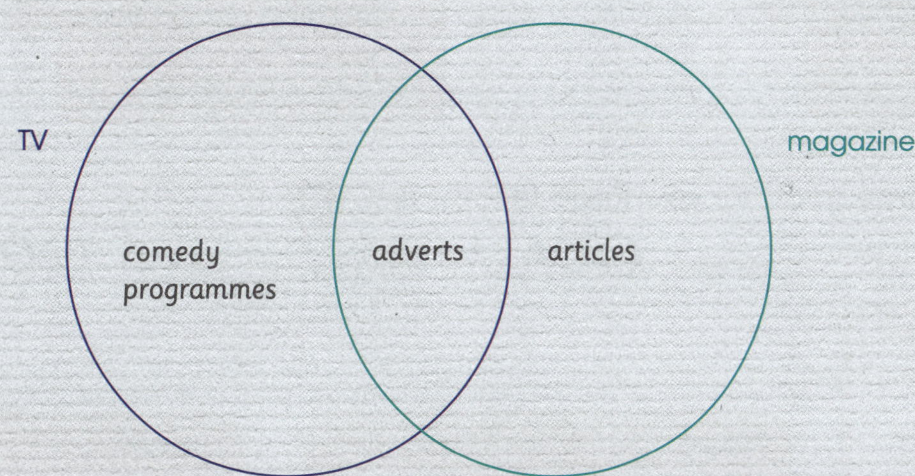

2 Thinking skills Work with a partner. Decide which way of presenting information would be best for each of these examples.

1 Answering the question: What do we use computers for?
2 Showing which activities you can do inside and outside.
3 Showing which languages are similar to each other.
4 Showing the favourite place of each person in your class.

3 Now choose one of the examples in Activity 2. Work with a partner to present information.

Study skills: setting goals

1 Read and discuss. Whole Class

1 A 'goal' is something that you want to achieve. Do you have any goals to improve your learning?

2 Do you write down these goals?

2 Look at these goals. Find this information.

1 What's the goal?

2 When do they want to achieve the goal?

3 What will they do?

4 How will they know if they have achieved the goal?

GOAL?
I want to improve my intonation skills this month.

How?
I will listen carefully in class. I will concentrate when I repeat. I will always try again when I say something wrong.

Check?
My teacher will understand 90% of my English. My teacher will say that my intonation is improving.

GOAL?
I want to finish my homework on time this month.

How?
I will start my homework when I arrive home. I won't look out of the window. I will look at the clock.

Check?
I will give my teacher my homework on time all month.

3 Now write some goals for you. Read the tips first. me

Tips

- Remember to make your goals realistic.
- Remember to say when you want to achieve the goal.

GOAL?

How?

Check?

GOAL?

How?

Check?

4 Thinking skills Show your goals to a partner. Answer these questions about your partner's goals. Can you improve your goals?

1 Is the goal clear and realistic?

2 Does the goal say when they want to achieve it?

3 How will they achieve the goal?

4 How will they check if they achieve the goal?

1 Read and discuss.

Whole Class

1 How do you research information on the Internet?

2 How do you know that the information you find is correct?

2 Find the answers to these questions on the Internet.

1 How far is Puerto Rico from New York?

______

2 Which country produces the most bananas?

______

3 How much is £100 in dollars?

______

4 Whose faces are on the £5 banknote?

______

3 Work with a partner. Answer these questions.

1 Are your answers the same? Did you visit the same websites?

______

2 How did you decide what the best answer was?

______

4 Thinking skills Read the tips. Which do you do already? Which is the most useful?

Researching information

Tips for researching information on the Internet

Tip 1: Don't always click on the first result you see. Scroll down to find a website that you think will have useful information.

Tip 2: Look at the address before you click. Maybe it is a website you have used before, or one that your teacher recommends.

Tip 3: Remember that you shouldn't believe everything you read. It is good to check information on more than one website.

Tip 4: If it is possible, check the date that the information was written. Is it too old to be useful? Can you find newer information in another place?

Tip 5: Make a note of the website where you found the information. This way, you can find the information again if you have to check it.

5 Now use these tips to research this information.

1 What different materials did the Romans make coins from?

______

2 What is the most valuable Roman coin? How much is it worth now?

______

3 Which tips did you use?

______

8 Study skills: managing your time

1 Read and discuss.

Whole Class

1 Do you always do everything that you need to do each day?

2 What do you do to help you manage your time?

2 Thinking skills Look at how you use your time. Then compare your record with a partner's.

1 Keep a record for two days. Write down everything you do in every hour of the day. Include eating, sleeping, studying, etc. Use a chart like this one.

2 Be honest! The more honest you are, the more useful the chart will be!

3 Look at the chart and ask yourself these questions:

What did I want to do, but I didn't have time?

When could I do it?

3 Read these suggestions. Do you think they will help you? Discuss them with your partner.

1 Write a priority list of what you need to do today and the rest of the week. This can include schoolwork, hobbies and family events. Decide if each task is A, B or C:

A = Important and urgent   B = Important, but not urgent   C = Not important or urgent

2 Think about how long each task will take. Do you usually think that you can do a task more quickly than you actually do? Remember to add more time!

3 Keep a task calendar. There are many electronic calendars you can use. Put your tasks into the calendar. Put the As first, then the Bs, then the Cs.

4 Make sure you review your calendar every day. What have I done? What do I have to add? What do I have to move?

4 Now plan your time for a week. After a week, answer and discuss these questions with your class.

1 Did I manage my time successfully?

____

2 What worked well and why?

____

3 What didn't work well and why?

____

4 What have I learnt about how I manage my time?

____

1 Read and discuss.

Whole Class

1 Do you worry when you have tests or exams?

2 What happens to you when you're nervous?

2 Look at these pictures. How often do these things happen when you have important things to do? Read and answer.

1 = always 2 = often 3 = sometimes 4 = never

1

I have a headache. ☐

2

I'm in a bad mood. ☐

3

I have a stomach ache. ☐

4

I don't sleep very well. ☐

5

I don't feel very hungry. ☐

6

I feel worried and upset. ☐

3 Here are some tips to help you. Read and tick the things that you do now.

Here are some things you can do when you are feeling stressed or nervous:

- If you have a test, study every day. Don't do all the work on the last day. ☐
- Try to go to bed early. ☐
- Do exercise and do sport. It's a good way to relax your body. ☐
- Drink water. It is important to be hydrated. ☐
- Talk to an adult and share your worries. ☐
- In the test, remember that you will try your best. Don't think 'I can't do this!'. ☐
- In the test, look at all the questions and do the easier ones first. ☐
- If you feel nervous in the test, drink some water and try to breathe slowly. ☐

4 Write a plan to manage your stress.

When I'm nervous, I ______________________________

The next time I feel nervous before a test I can ______________________________

The next time I feel nervous in a test I can ______________________________

Listening

1 Listen. For each question, choose the correct answer.

CD4 28

1 You will hear two friends talking about a museum they went to. What did he think?

A He wouldn't like to go again.

B The museum was surprisingly good.

C The rooms about history were too scary.

2 You will hear a girl telling her friend about her train trip? How did she feel about it?

A Disappointed that she missed the train.

B Happy that she enjoyed the trip.

C Angry that the train didn't wait for her.

3 You will hear two friends talking about riding a bike. The boy advises the girl to

A Start cycling with a small bike.

B Be careful on the road.

C Practise in the park.

4 You will hear two friends talking about a film they've seen. They agree that

A There was too much music.

B It was very funny.

C The end was good.

Writing

2 Your English teacher has asked you to write a story. Your story must begin with this sentence:

I was excited and nervous as I got on the train.

In your notebook, write your story in about 100 words.

Exam help — Learning to learn

Q: What do I need to think about before I start?

A: Read the sentence carefully. Make sure you write this story in the first person, for example. Think about the different tenses you can use, e.g. past simple and past continuous.

Listening

1 You will hear a radio interview with a young gymnast called Clare. Listen and for each question, choose the correct answer. CD4 29

1 Clare started gymnastics
A when she was three.
B when she started school.
C after she started school.

2 Clare trains
A four or five times a week.
B three times a week.
C every day.

3 What does Clare think of gymnastics competitions?
A They're stressful.
B They're too long.
C They're good fun.

4 In the last competition, Clare
A won a gold medal.
B won a silver medal.
C didn't win a medal.

5 When Clare isn't doing gymnastics, she enjoys
A hanging out with friends.
B shopping.
C reading mystery stories.

6 What does Clare want to do in the future?
A Compete in the Olympic Games.
B She isn't sure.
C Become a gymnastics teacher.

Writing

2 You see this notice in a sports magazine. Write your article in about 100 words.

Articles wanted!
Sports fun!
Tell us about a sport you enjoy. *How long have you done it?*
What equipment do you need and how do you play it? *Why do you like it?*
Write an article answering these questions and we will publish the most interesting articles in our magazine.

____
____
____
____
____

Exam help Learning to learn
Q: What do I need to do when I read the notice?
A: It's important to identify all the questions in the notice. Make sure you answer each question when you write your article.

Listening

1 **Listen and complete the notes. Write one or two words or a number or a date or a time.**

CD4 30

Rushton Green Club

When: Saturday and (1) ______________ mornings. 10am to (2) ______________

Place: On the corner of Mill Lane and (3) ______________________________.

Contact: Mr (4) ______________ in room (5) ______________.

Bring: Boots and (6) ______________.

Writing

2 **Read this email from your English-speaking friend Bella, and the notes you have made. In your notebook, write your answer in about 100 words. Use all the notes.**

To: ______________

From: Bella

Hi! It's great to hear from you again. Which film did you go and see in the end? Was it good? Would you recommend it?

Anyway. I have some great news! I'm coming to see you in July.

I'm staying with my parents but I will be very near. What days can we see each other? Where could we meet?

Look forward to seeing you soon.

Bella

Notes:
- Say which one
- Tell Bella
- Great!
- Suggest some dates and places

Exam help — **Learning to learn**

Q: What are the most important things to think about?

A: Imagine the email is written to you. Remember to separate your text into short paragraphs. Don't forget to say hello and goodbye!

Exams Practice

1 **Listen. For each question, choose the correct answer.** CD4 31

1 Which kind of film are Peter and Jo going to see?

A

B

C

2 Where was Ana last night?

A

B

C

3 What can you watch at seven o'clock?

A

B

C

2 **You see this notice in a film magazine. In your notebook, write your article in about 100 words.**

Articles wanted!

Fantastic films!

Tell us about a film you love.

What kind of film is it? *Who are the characters and what is it about?* *Why do you recommend it?*

Write an article and we will publish the most interesting articles in our magazine.

Exam help

Learning to learn

Q: How can I make my article more interesting?

A: A good way to keep the reader's interest is to use WOW words. For example, *incredible, amazing, exciting, fantastic, funny*.

Listening

1 **You will hear an interview about a young boy who volunteers his time to old people. Listen and for each question, choose the correct answer.** CD4 32

1 Oliver's grandmother
A can't see very well.
B can't hear very well.
C can't move very well.

2 Oliver liked reading to his grandmother because
A her friends were always very kind.
B he had a very clear voice.
C it helped him find out about world news.

3 At Talking News,
A most of the volunteers are over 60.
B many of the volunteers are young people.
C they don't allow volunteers who are over 60.

4 Oliver goes to the studio
A every week.
B every two weeks.
C every three weeks.

5 Oliver knows that his grandmother likes
A different types of books.
B detective stories.
C historical novels.

6 What does Oliver want to do when he grows up?
A Have a job in radio.
B Be a detective.
C He isn't sure.

Writing

2 **Read this email from your English-speaking friend Mark, and the notes you have made. In your notebook, write your answer in about 100 words. Use all the notes.**

To: ____________
From: Mark
Hello. How are you? Are you having a good weekend? — *Answer the questions*
Can you tell me more about your new blog? What is the blog about? — *Tell Mark*
Did you decide to write about music, films or travel?
What are you going to write next? — *Tell Mark about your plans* Maybe I could write something for your blog, too. Can you suggest something? — *Suggest some things Mark could write*
I love writing!
I hope to see you soon.
Mark

Listening

1 **You will hear a woman telling a group of students about her work as an astronaut. Listen and complete the notes. Write one or two words or a number or a date or a time.**

CD4 33

Astronaut

- Susan has travelled to space (1)________ times.
- Astronauts need to study a (2) ________ degree.
- Astronauts are about (3) ________ when they start space training.
- Astronauts have to speak English and (4) ________ very well.
- It's important to (5) ________ every day in space.
- Astronauts need to be sociable because the living space is (6) ________.

Writing

2 **Your English teacher has asked you to write a story. Your story must begin with this sentence:**

Peter slowly opened the box.

Write your story in about 100 words.

____

____

____

____

____

____

____

____

____

Exam help

Learning to learn

Q: How should I organise my story?

A: All stories need a beginning, a middle and an end. It's a good idea to plan your story before you start writing.

Listening

1 **Listen. For each question, choose the correct answer.** CD4 34

1 You will hear two friends talking about a skateboarding competition. How did the girl feel?

A Disappointed not to be in the competition. ☐

B Happy that Jimmy won the competition. ☐

C Angry that she hurt her leg. ☐

2 You will hear two friends talking about a new café. They agree that

A The café is always full of people. ☐

B The chocolate milkshake is amazing. ☐

C They'll go there again tomorrow. ☐

3 You will hear two friends talking about a new club at school. The girl suggests to the boy that

A He comes to the judo club next week. ☐

B He plays volleyball or badminton next week. ☐

C Judo isn't fast enough for him. ☐

4 You will hear two friends talking about buying a present for their friend. They agree that

A Harry would like a T-shirt for his birthday. ☐

B Harry would like the new adventure book for his birthday. ☐

C Harry likes reading. ☐

Writing

2 **You see this notice on an international English-language website.**

Fascinating hobbies

Do you have an interesting hobby? Maybe it is something you started a long time ago. Tell us all about it.
What do you like about it? When and how do you do it? How would you recommend it to other people?

Write an article answering these questions. We will publish the best one!

In your notebook, write your article in about 100 words.

Exam help — Learning to learn

Q: Can you give me three tips?

A: (i) Think of a good title to get people interested. (ii) Divide your article into short paragraphs. Each should have a different idea. (iii) Make sure that you answer all the questions. You will lose marks if you do not.

Listening

1 You will hear a radio presenter talking about a competition. Listen and complete the notes. Write one or two words or a number or a date or a time. CD4 35

Story writing competition

- The competition has been organised by the (1) ______________.
- The competition is for children aged between 7 and (2) ______________.
- The competition closes on (3) ______________.
- Every author receives (4) ______________.
- There are (5) ______________ books for the winners.
- The town newspaper will publish the (6) ______________.

Writing

2 Read this email from your English-speaking friend Emma, and the notes you have made. In your notebook, write your answer in about 100 words. Use all the notes.

To: ______________

From: Emma

Hi. How are you? I hope you had a good weekend. [Fantastic!]

Do you remember that we talked about going to the beach? Well, my dad says he can take us this weekend? Are you free to do it? [Yes – say which day]

In the morning, we can go sailing or surfing. Which do you prefer? [Tell Emma]

What would you like to do in the afternoon? [Suggest …]

See you soon.

Emma

Exam help Learning to learn

Q: What do I need to check when I've finished writing?

A: Read through your email to check that you've answered all the questions and it makes sense. Then read it again carefully to check your spelling and punctuation.

Listening

1 Listen. For each question, choose the correct answer.

CD4 36

1 Where's the girl's pencil case?

A

B

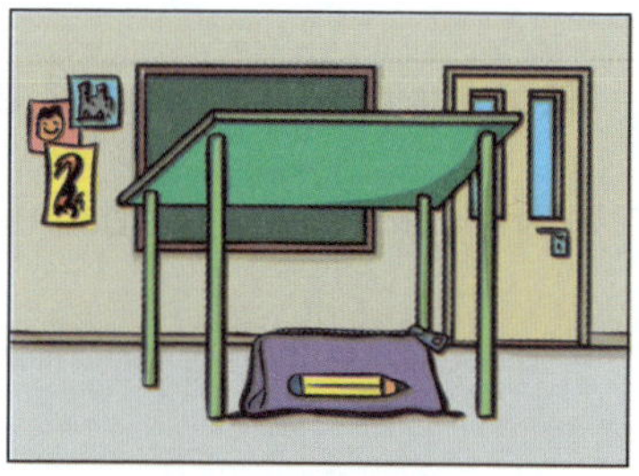

C

2 Which activity does the boy want to do?

A

B

C

3 Which subject does the girl have at 9am tomorrow?

A

B

C

Writing

2 Your English teacher has asked you to write a story. Your story must begin with this sentence:

It was Beth's first day at secondary school.

In your notebook, write your story in about 100 words.

Exam help

Learning to learn

Q: What can I do if I haven't got any ideas?

A: Don't worry. Ask yourself some questions and write down your ideas. *How does Beth feel? What's the school like? Who does she meet? What happens next?*

Speaking

Unit 1

Work with a partner.

1 Ask and answer these general questions about yourself.

1 Where do you live?

2 What do you do after school?

3 What do you do at the weekend?

4 What activities do you like doing?

2 Look at the pictures. They show different types of travel. What can you see in the pictures? Tell your partner.

Pupil A

Pupil B

3 The photographs show different types of travel. Talk about how you like to travel. Use the questions to help you.

1 Which form of travel do you prefer? Why?

2 Do you like travelling? Why? / Why not?

3 How do you travel to school? Do you enjoy it? Why? / Why not?

Unit 2

Work with a partner.

1 Ask and answer these general questions about yourself.

1 What is your favourite sport?

2 Are there any sports you don't like?

3 What do you prefer to do in your free time?

4 Do you have any hobbies? What are they?

2 Your school has decided to buy some new sports equipment. Talk together about the equipment you see in the pictures. Choose three you think your school should buy and say why.

1

2

3

4

5

6
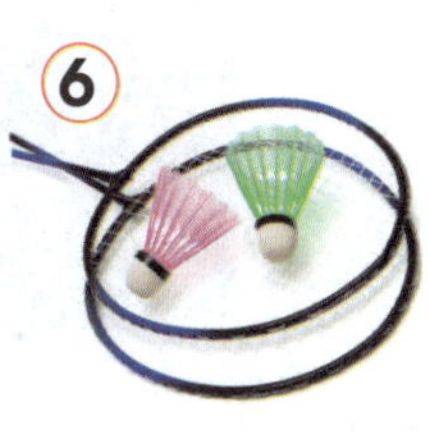

3 The photographs show different types of sports equipment. Talk about which sports you like. Use the questions to help you.

1 Which of the sports in Activity 2 do you prefer? Why?

2 Which sport would you like to try in the future? Why?

3 Which sport do you enjoy doing? Why?

Watch the Exam Resources Video

Unit 3

Speaking

Work with a partner.

1 Ask and answer the questions.

1 Describe your favourite food.

2 What food don't you like?

3 Do you like eating in restaurants?

4 Do you like cooking? Why? / Why not?

2 Look at the pictures. They show different ways of keeping healthy. What can you see in the pictures? Tell your partner.

3 The photographs show different ways of keeping healthy. Talk about how you like to keep healthy. Use the questions to help you.

1 What do you do to keep healthy?

2 What is your favourite type of exercise?

3 Do you have any unhealthy habits? Can you improve them?

Unit 4

Work with a partner.

1 Ask and answer the questions.

1 Do you prefer reading books or comics?

2 What is your favourite film?

3 What creative activity do you enjoy doing?

4 Do you play computer games?

2 You and a friend are going to take up a new creative activity. Talk together about the different activities you can do and say which one would be most interesting.

3 The photographs show different creative activities. Talk about creative activities you do. Use the questions to help you.

1 What creative hobby do you do?

2 Do you prefer group activities or doing activities on your own? Why?

3 Do you prefer activities that use a computer or your hands? Why?

4 Why are creative hobbies good for you?

Watch the Exam Resources Video

Speaking

Unit 5

Work with a partner.

1 Ask and answer the questions.

1 Do you enjoy reading or writing stories?

2 Do you read blogs? What are they about?

3 Do you prefer newspapers or magazines?

4 How do you communicate with your friends and family?

2 Look at the pictures. They show different forms of communication. What can you see in the pictures? Tell your partner.

3 The photographs show different forms of communication. Talk about how you communicate with friends and family. Use the questions to help you.

1 What form of communication do you prefer?

2 How do you use your computer to communicate?

3 Do you prefer sending text messages or talking on the telephone? Why?

Unit 6

Work with a partner.

1 Ask and answer the questions.

1 What is your favourite subject at school?

2 Do you enjoy going to school? Why? / Why not?

3 What do you want to do when you finish school? Why?

4 Do you think you will get married? Why? / Why not?

2 You and a friend are going to make a poster about an interesting job. Talk together about the jobs in the pictures and say which one would be most interesting.

3 The photographs show different types of jobs. Talk about which job you would like to do. Use the questions to help you.

1 Would you like to be an archaeologist? Why / Why not?

2 Which job wouldn't you like to do? Why?

3 What three things would you like to do in the future?

Watch the Exam Resources Video

Speaking

Unit 7

Work with a partner.

1 Ask and answer the questions.

1 Do you save money?
2 What do you buy with your savings?
3 Where do you prefer to shop?
4 Do you buy things online? What do you buy?

2 Look at the pictures. They show different places to shop. What can you see in the pictures? Tell your partner.

Pupil A

Pupil B

3 The photographs show different places to shop. Talk about your shopping habits. Use the questions to help you.

1 How often do you go shopping?
2 Where do you like to go shopping?
3 What kinds of things can you buy online?
4 Would you buy things from a second-hand shop? Why? / Why not?

Unit 8

Work with a partner.

1 Ask and answer the questions.

1 What do you do with your friends after school?
2 Where do you usually go at weekends?
3 Would you like to visit a tropical island? Why? / Why not?
4 Would you like to travel in space? Why? / Why not?

2 You and a friend are going to a tropical island. Talk about the different things you can do there and choose one you would like to do together.

1

2

3

4

3 The photographs show different things you can do on a tropical island. Talk about other things you could do on a tropical island. Use the questions to help you.

1 Would you go shopping on a tropical island? Why? / Why not?
2 Would you go sailing? Why? / Why not?
3 Would you help to clean up a beach? Why? / Why not?

Watch the Exam Resources Video

Unit 9

Speaking

Work with a partner.

1 Ask and answer the questions.

1 Tell us about a teacher you like.

2 How often do you use a mobile phone?

3 Which do you like the best, the morning or the afternoon? Why?

4 How do you usually spend your holidays?

2 Look at the pictures. They show schools in the past and now. What can you see in the pictures? Tell your partner.

Pupil A

Pupil B

3 The photographs show different types of schools. Talk together about the different schools and say which one you think is the most interesting.

4 The photographs show different types of school. Talk about why education is important. Use the questions to help you.

1 What do you learn at school?

2 What is the best thing about school?

3 Do you want to go to university? Why? / Why not?

Watch the Exam Resources Video

Irregular Verbs

Infinitive	Past simple	Past participle
be	was / were	been
blow	blew	blown
break	broke	broken
build	built	built
buy	bought	bought
choose	chose	chosen
come	came	come
cut	cut	cut
do	did	done
draw	drew	drawn
drink	drank	drunk
eat	ate	eaten
feel	felt	felt
find	found	found
fly	flew	flown
give	gave	given
go	went	been / gone
grow	grew	grown
have	had	had
know	knew	known
learn	learnt / learned	learnt / learned
lose	lost	lost
make	made	made
meet	met	met
put	put	put
read	read	read
ride	rode	ridden
run	ran	run
say	said	said
see	saw	seen
sell	sold	sold
sing	sang	sung
sit	sat	sat
swim	swam	swum
take	took	taken
tell	told	told
think	thought	thought
wear	wore	worn
win	won	won
write	wrote	written

Infinitive		Past simple		Past participle	
English	My language	English	My language	English	My language
be	______	was/were	______	been	______
blow	______	blew	______	blown	______
buy	______	bought	______	bought	______
cut	______	cut	______	cut	______
do	______	did	______	done	______
drink	______	drank	______	drunk	______
eat	______	ate	______	eaten	______
find	______	found	______	found	______
go	______	went	______	been/gone	______
grow	______	grew	______	grown	______
have	______	had	______	had	______
know	______	knew	______	known	______
learn	______	learnt/learned	______	learnt/learned	______
make	______	made	______	made	______
meet	______	met	______	met	______
put	______	put	______	put	______
read	______	read	______	read	______
ride	______	rode	______	ridden	______
see	______	saw	______	seen	______
sell	______	sold	______	sold	______
sing	______	sang	______	sung	______
swim	______	swam	______	swum	______
take	______	took	______	taken	______
wear	______	wore	______	worn	______
win	______	won	______	won	______
write	______	wrote	______	written	______

Macmillan Education
4 Crinan Street
London N1 9XW

A division of Macmillan Publishers Limited
Companies and representatives throughout the world

Activity Book ISBN 978-1-380-01381-1

This edition published 2018

First edition entitled *High Five! English* published 2014 by Macmillan Publishers Limited

Series concept design by Tom Cole
Page make-up by emc design ltd
Illustrated by Martyn Cain, Phil Garner, Ángeles Peinador (Beehive Illustration), Mark Ruffle (Beehive Illustration), Dave Smith, Dusan Pavlic (Beehive Illustration), Andy Keylock (Beehive Illustration)
Cover design by Bigtop Design Limited
Cover photograph by Getty Images/Uppercut RF/Jules Frazier Photography, Getty Image/Bob Abraham, Getty Images/hadynyah, Macmillan Publishing Ltd/Lisa Payne, Macmillan Publishing Ltd/Tom Dick and Debbie Productions
Picture research by Victoria Gaunt; Fernanda Rocha/Ikonia LLC.
Songs produced and arranged by Footsteps and Tom Dick & Debbie Productions

Authors' acknowledgements
The authors would like to thank everyone at Macmillan who has given help and advice throughout this project. Special thanks from Rob to Belén, Natalia, Xana and Pablo for all their inspiration. Special thanks from Donna to José, Elisa, Teresa and Marina for their encouragement and enthusiasm.

Acknowledgements
The publishers would like to thank the following teachers for their contribution to the project:
Ana Postigo, CEIP Vicálvaro, Madrid; Beatriz García Vaquero, CEIP Mariano José de Larra, Madrid; Damián Quiralte Fresneda, CEIP Claudio Moyano, Madrid; Eamonn Healy, Colegio SEK Santa Isabel, Madrid; Elvira Robledo Gandarias, Colegio Ayalde, Loiu, Vizcaya; Francisco Javier Navarro Pineda, Colegio Tajamar, Madrid; Guiomar Yagüe Martínez, CEIP Celso Emilio Ferreiro, Móstoles, Madrid; Henar Del Gallo Muñoz, CEIP Cantos Altos, Collado Villalba, Madrid; Ignacio de la Puente Rodríguez, CEIP El Cantizal, Las Rozas, Madrid; Inmaculada Romero Fanego, CEIP Príncipes de Asturias, Pozuelo de Alarcón, Madrid; Laura Tenorio, CEIP Esperanza, Madrid; María del Rosario García Leal , CEIP Rufino Blanco, Madrid; Patricia Sanz, CEIP Félix Rodríguez de la Fuente, Coslada, Madrid; Silvia San José Paul, CEIP El Cantizal, Las Rozas, Madrid; Víctor Molinero Cuartango, CEIP Ciudad de Roma, Madrid; Virginia Escalona Monreal, CEIP La Encina, Las Rozas, Madrid; Laura Zarzuelo, Colegio Virgen de la Almudena, Collado Villalba, Madrid; Eugenio Domínguez, Colegio Virgen de la Almudena, Collado Villalba, Madrid; Silvia Díez de Rivera, Colegio Orvalle, Las Rozas, Madrid; Maite Crespo, Colegio Jesús Nazareno, Madrid; Rocío González, Colegio Jesús Nazareno, Madrid; Silvia Valderrama, CEIP Benito Pérez Galdós, Arganda del Rey, Madrid; Lilian Villafuerte, CEIP Rosa Chacel, Collado Villalba, Madrid; Cristina Baeza, CEIP Rosa Chacel, Collado Villalba, Madrid; Carlota Padovani, CEIP Vicálvaro, Madrid; Leyre, Alcalde CEIP Cortes de Cádiz, Madrid; María Andrés, Colegio Matter Inmaculata, Madrid.

The author and publishers would like to thank the following for permission to reproduce their images:

Alamy Stock Photo/agStock Images, Inc p28(bcr), Alamy Stock Photo/Anatolii Babii p132(tr), Alamy Stock Photo/Blend Images p94, Alamy Stock Photo/Aleksey Boldin p131(tr), Alamy Stock Video/Ashley Cooper p15(l), Alamy Stock Photo/Guy Corbishley p117(tr), Alamy/Andrew Desmond p5(tr), Alamy Stock Photo/fStop Images GmbH p41(br), Alamy Stock Photo/F1online digitale Bildagentur GmbH p92(c), Alamy Stock Photo/Christoph Hermann p75(cr), Alamy Stock Photo/Hero Images Inc. p66(tr), Alamy Stock Photo/imageBROKER pp133(tr), 18(tr), Alamy Stock Photo/iPics Photography p85(tr), Alamy Stock Photo/Richard Levine p63(b), Alamy Stock Photo/Library of Congress/S.Dupuis p91(br), Alamy Stock Photo/Francisco Martinez p84(cr), Alamy Stock Photo/Mint Images Limited p41(cr), Alamy Stock Photo/moodboard p96, Alamy Stock Photo/PjrStudio p117(br), Alamy Stock Photo/PCN Photography p73, Alamy Stock Photo/Niels Quist p133(tl), Alamy Stock Photo/Simon Reddy p27(cr), Alamy Stock Photo/S.E.A. Photo p95(tr), Alamy Stock Photo/Alex Segre pp40(tcr), 131(tl), 132(tl), Alamy Stock Photo/jeremy sutton-hibbert p60(cr), Alamy Stock Photo/Peter Titmuss p133(cr), Alamy Stock Photo/Tetra Images p34(tr); **Getty Images** p5(cr), Getty Images/Eric Audras p56(c), Getty Images/Greg Bajor p14, Getty Images/Blend Images – Kidstock p49, Getty Images/blueenayim p134(background), Getty Images/Caiaimage/Sam Edwards p116, Getty Images/Cheryl Chenet p92(cr), Getty Images/Dan77 p10(cr), Getty Images/Dave2003 p75(tr), Getty Images/deniseedgellslark p130(4), Getty Images/DigitalVision/Jetta Productions p59(cr), Getty Images/Echo p53, Getty Images/E+/Mark Bowden p71(tr), Getty Images/E+/vpopovic p120-128(top banner), Getty Images/Chris Fertnig p93, Getty Images/Fotosearch p38, Getty Images/Fuse p24(tr), Getty Images/Gamma-Rapho/Francis Demange p8(cr), Getty Images/Tony Garcia p51, Getty Images/H. Armstrong Roberts/ClassicStock p91(tr), Getty Images/Hero Images p130(3), Getty Images/Nancy Honey p89(tr), Getty Images/Image Source p132(1), Getty Images/Imgorthand p115, Getty Images/iStock/Mishella p81(cr), Getty Images/iStockphoto/scanrail p47(bml), Getty Images/Juice Images p133(bl), Getty Images/KatarzynaBialasiewicz p131(3), Getty Images/kupicoo p29, Getty Images/John Lamparski p22, Getty Images/Lunasix p129(5), Getty Images/Milatas p130(2), Getty Images/MMADIA p3(background-tr), Getty Images/monkeybusinessimages p95(br), Getty Images/Nadezhda1906 p132(2), Getty Images/National Geographic/Matt Moyer p81(tr), Getty Images/Jose Luis Pelaez Inc p129(tl), Getty/pilotka p17(br), Getty Images/Pixland/Jupiterimages p59(tr), Getty Images/Popperfoto/Bob Thomas p11(br), Getty Images/Eliza Snow p17(cr), Getty Images/Stockbyte/Jupiterimages p19(tr), Getty Images/ultramarinfoto p132(4), Getty Images/Uwe Umstaetter p54, Getty Images/ViewStock p129(tr), Getty Images/Kathrin Ziegler p71(br); **Goodshoot** p83; **Image Source**/Sonya Farrell p19(br); **Image 100** p9(cr); **Macmillan Publishers Ltd.**/Dave Cockburn p89(2-bml); **PhotoDisc**/Getty Images ppp46(bc), 129(3); **REX**/Shutterstock/Carlos De Saa/Epa p21(cr), REX/Shutterstock/Dreamworks Animation/Kobal p18(br), REX/Shutterstock/David Fisher p21(tr), REX/Shutterstock/Studio Ghibli/Kobal p40(bcr); **Shutterstock**/Ruth Black p48(1), Shutterstock/ESUN7756 p85(br), Shutterstock/Juice Images Ltd p130(6), Shutterstock/LuckyImages p130(tr), Shutterstock/MrNovel p130(1), Shutterstock/Sergey Nivens p37, Shutterstock/Martin Novak p17(tr), Shutterstock/Maksym Poriechkin p130(tl), Shutterstock/Rawpixel.com p131(6), Shutterstock/Oleksandr Rybitskiy p47(tmr), Shutterstock/Suzanne Tucker p89(2-br), Shutterstock/Bielikov Vadym p15(r), Shutterstock/XEG p131(1), Shutterstock/9091086 p133(br); **Stockdisc** p31; **Up the Resolution** p28(tcr); **123RF**/Solomin Andrey p89(2-tl), 123RF/auremar p131(4), 123RF/Oleg Beloborodov p133(cl), 123RF/blotty p47(bl), 123RF/BlueOrange Studio p132(3), 123RF/chrisrt p129(2), 123RF/Mike Flippo p129(4), 123RF/goodluz p131(2), 123RF/Andreas Kostner p47(tr), 123RF/Andrei Krauchuk p47(br), 123RF/luca lago p89(2-tmr), 123RF/margouillat p79, 123RF/Alberto Masnovo p129(1), 123RF/Sergey Mironov p47(bmr), 123RF/PaylessImages p47(tml), 123RF/Roy Pedersen p130(5), 123RF/Andriy Popov p131(5), 123RF/Olga Popova p89(2-tml), 123RF/Sascha Preussner p89(2-bl), 123RF/scanrail p47(tl), 123RF/Boris Sosnovyy p89(2-tr), 123RF/Igor Tarasyuk p89(2-bmr), 123RF/igor terekhov p129(6), 123RF/vvoennyy p57.

Commissioned photographs by Lisa Payne/Macmillan Publishers Ltd: pp 1, 3, 14(br), 24(br), 34(br), 46(br), 56(br), 66(br), 78(br), 88(cr, br), 98(br), 120(cr).

Printed and bound in Spain
2022 2021 2020 2019 2018
10 9 8 7 6 5 4 3 2 1